SCOTT FORESMAN
Reading Street
COMMON CORE

W9-BSD-248

Reading Street
Common Core
Writing
to Sources

Glenview, Illinois

Boston, Massachusetts

Chandler, Arizona

Upper Saddle River, New Jersey

ALWAYS LEARNING

PEARSON

ISBN-13: 978-0-328-76856-1
ISBN-10:   0-328-76856-1

7 8 9 10 V0N4 16 15 14

Reading Street Common Core
Writing to Sources

Reading Street Common Core Writing to Sources makes fact-finding fun! Students substantiate their claims and communicate in writing what they have learned from one text and then from other related texts.

Reading Street Common Core Writing to Sources encourages students to collaborate and share their growing knowledge with peers, adding quality experiences in the art of using text-based evidence.

Reading Street Common Core Writing to Sources provides more practice with all modes of writing—argument, informative/explanatory, and narrative— and connects to the Common Core State Standards.

Reading Street Common Core Writing to Sources gives students opportunities to complete Performance Tasks by writing in response to what they read and collaborating with others.

Reading Street Common Core Writing to Sources offers you an alternative approach to writing tasks on Reading Street!

1 Write Like a Reporter
Write to one source.
Students respond to the main selection by citing evidence from the text.

2 Connect the Texts
Write to two sources.
Students respond to the main and paired selections by citing evidence from the texts.

3 Prove It! Unit Writing Task
Write to multiple sources.
Students analyze multiple sources within a unit and cite evidence from the texts.

4 More Connect the Texts
Additional lessons specific to writing forms within all modes of writing—argument, informative/explanatory, and narrative—are included.

"Write Like a Reporter!"

Table of Contents

Get Ready for Performance Tasks

Unit 1 Exploration

Writing Focus: Narrative

Name_____

Write Like a Reporter
Narrative Paragraph

Student Prompt Reread pages 28–32 of *The Twin Club* and look at the pictures. Describe the relationship between the two boys, and include a description of the boys' summer experiences with Grandma Inés.

_____

_____

_____

_____

_____

_____

_____

_____

_____

_____

_____

_____

_____

_____

_____

_____

Write Like a Reporter
Narrative Paragraph

> **Student Prompt, p. 6** Reread pages 28–32 of *The Twin Club* and look at the pictures. Describe the relationship between the two boys, and include a description of the boys' summer experiences with Grandma Inés.

Writing to Sources Remind children that both the pictures and the words in a story provide information about the plot and the characters, including their thoughts and feelings. As children reread the story, have them list clues and details they will use in their writing. Remind them to include details that describe what the boys have done together and how they feel about each other. Have children put the story events in order, using words such as *first, next, then, later,* and *afterward.*

Children's paragraphs should:

- provide a setting, narrator, and characters
- include a chronology of events that reflects those in the text
- use descriptive words and sensory details in the retelling of events
- demonstrate strong command of the conventions of standard written English

---

© **Common Core State Standards**

Writing 3. Write narratives in which they recount a well-elaborated event or short sequence of events, include details to describe actions, thoughts, and feelings, use temporal words to signal event order, and provide a sense of closure.

Connect the Texts

Narrative Poem

Student Prompt Reread pages 36–41 of *The Twin Club.* Pretend you are Juan Ramón and write a poem to send to Jorge that describes where Juan Ramón lives and what he likes about his home. Use the poems "The 1st Day of School" and "The 179th Day of School" as models for the form and language in your poem.

_____

- -

_____

- -

_____

- -

_____

- -

_____

- -

_____

- -

_____

- -

_____

- -

_____

- -

_____

Connect the Texts
Narrative Poem

Student Prompt, p. 8 Reread pages 36–41 of *The Twin Club*. Pretend you are Juan Ramón and write a poem to send to Jorge that describes where Juan Ramón lives and what he likes about his home. Use the poems "The 1st Day of School" and "The 179th Day of School" as models for the form and language in your poem.

Writing to Sources As children develop their poems, encourage them to look for words in *The Twin Club* that help them visualize what Juan Ramón experiences when he returns home. Point out that because the poems "The 1st Day of School" and "The 179th Day of School" both contain sensory details about attending school, it is easy to visualize what is happening on that first school day and on the last school day. Discuss the adjectives used in the poems and how they clarify and strengthen the images the poems provide *(the unchipped chalk, scuffed-up shoes)*.

4-point Narrative Writing Rubric					
Score	**Narrative Focus**	**Organization**	**Development of Narrative**	**Language and Vocabulary**	**Conventions**
4	Narrative is clearly focused and developed throughout.	Narrative has a well-developed, logical, easy-to-follow plot.	Narrative includes thorough and effective use of details, dialogue, and description.	Narrative uses precise, concrete sensory language as well as figurative language and/or domain-specific vocabulary.	Narrative has correct grammar, usage, spelling, capitalization, and punctuation.
3	Narrative is mostly focused and developed throughout.	Narrative has a plot, but there may be some lack of clarity and/or unrelated events.	Narrative includes adequate use of details, dialogue and description.	Narrative uses adequate sensory and figurative language and/or domain-specific vocabulary.	Narrative has a few errors but is completely understandable.
2	Narrative is somewhat developed but may occasionally lose focus.	Narrative's plot is difficult to follow, and ideas are not connected well.	Narrative includes only a few details, dialogues, and descriptions.	Language in narrative is not precise or sensory; lacks domain-specific vocabulary.	Narrative has some errors in usage, grammar, spelling and/or punctuation.
1	Narrative may be confusing, unfocused, or too short.	Narrative has little or no apparent plot.	Narrative includes few or no details, dialogue or description.	Language in narrative is vague, unclear, or confusing.	Narrative is hard to follow because of frequent errors.
0	Narrative gets no credit if it does not demonstrate adequate command of narrative writing traits.				

© **Common Core State Standards**

Writing 3. Write narratives in which they recount a well-elaborated event or short sequence of events, include details to describe actions, thoughts, and feelings, use temporal words to signal event order, and provide a sense of closure.

Name_____

Write Like a Reporter
Narrative Diary Entry

Student Prompt Reread pages 66–69 in *Exploring Space with an Astronaut.* Using details from the photographs and text, write a simple diary entry describing one incident an astronaut has and how he or she feels about being in space.

_____

_____

_____

_____

_____

_____

_____

_____

_____

_____

_____

_____

_____

_____

_____

_____

_____

_____

Write Like a Reporter

Narrative Diary Entry

> **Student Prompt, p. 10** Reread pages 66–69 in *Exploring Space with an Astronaut.* Using details from the photographs and text, write a simple diary entry describing one incident an astronaut has and how he or she feels about being in space.

Writing to Sources Discuss with children the variety of information found in this expository text. Point out the labels on the photos and the details from the text. Tell children this information will help them develop a narrative describing an astronaut's personal experience during a flight in space.

Children's writing should:

- provide a setting, narrator, and/or characters
- have focus and include events that are true to those in the text
- use sensory details and descriptive words that identify the events
- demonstrate strong command of the conventions of standard written English

---

Ⓒ **Common Core State Standards**

Writing 3. Write narratives in which they recount a well-elaborated event or short sequence of events, include details to describe actions, thoughts, and feelings, use temporal words to signal event order, and provide a sense of closure.

Connect the Texts
Narrative Letter

Student Prompt Reread *Exploring Space with an Astronaut* and "A Trip to Space Camp." Pretend you are one of the children from Space Camp. Write a short letter to a real astronaut describing an experience you had at camp.

Connect the Texts
Narrative Letter

Student Prompt, p. 12 Reread *Exploring Space with an Astronaut* and "A Trip to Space Camp." Pretend you are one of the children from Space Camp. Write a short letter to a real astronaut describing an experience you had at camp.

Writing to Sources Explain to children that they need to carefully read each text. Details found in the labels, photographs, and text copy provide children with descriptions and precise words to help them write their letters.

4-point Narrative Writing Rubric					
Score	Narrative Focus	Organization	Development of Narrative	Language and Vocabulary	Conventions
4	Narrative is clearly focused and developed throughout.	Narrative has a well-developed, logical, easy-to-follow plot.	Narrative includes thorough and effective use of details, dialogue, and description.	Narrative uses precise, concrete sensory language as well as figurative language and/or domain-specific vocabulary.	Narrative has correct grammar, usage, spelling, capitalization, and punctuation.
3	Narrative is mostly focused and developed throughout.	Narrative has a plot, but there may be some lack of clarity and/or unrelated events.	Narrative includes adequate use of details, dialogue and description.	Narrative uses adequate sensory and figurative language and/or domain-specific vocabulary.	Narrative has a few errors but is completely understandable.
2	Narrative is somewhat developed but may occasionally lose focus.	Narrative's plot is difficult to follow, and ideas are not connected well.	Narrative includes only a few details, dialogues, and descriptions.	Language in narrative is not precise or sensory; lacks domain-specific vocabulary.	Narrative has some errors in usage, grammar, spelling and/or punctuation.
1	Narrative may be confusing, unfocused, or too short.	Narrative has little or no apparent plot.	Narrative includes few or no details, dialogue or description.	Language in narrative is vague, unclear, or confusing.	Narrative is hard to follow because of frequent errors.
0	Narrative gets no credit if it does not demonstrate adequate command of narrative writing traits.				

© **Common Core State Standards**

Writing 3. Write narratives in which they recount a well-elaborated event or short sequence of events, include details to describe actions, thoughts, and feelings, use temporal words to signal event order, and provide a sense of closure.

Name_____

Write Like a Reporter
Narrative Paragraph

Student Prompt Reread pages 96–99 in *Henry and Mudge and the Starry Night.* Look at the illustrations. Write a paragraph that adds more descriptive details to the story. Use the name of one of the characters and include what he or she sees or does.

_____
- -
_____
- -
_____
- -
_____
- -
_____
- -
_____
- -
_____
- -
_____
- -
_____
- -
_____
- -
_____
- -
_____

Write Like a Reporter
Narrative Paragraph

Student Prompt, p. 14 Reread pages 96–99 in *Henry and Mudge and the Starry Night.* Look at the illustrations. Write a paragraph that adds more descriptive details to the story. Use the name of one of the characters and include what he or she sees or does.

Writing to Sources Discuss how the author describes characters with details that allow children to visualize who the characters are, what they do, and where they do it. Explain to children that the illustrations help readers visualize the natural setting, while the text provides information about the animals that live there.

Children's paragraphs should:

- provide a setting and characters
- include events that are true to those in the text
- use descriptive words and details that identify the events
- demonstrate strong command of the conventions of standard written English

---

Ⓒ **Common Core State Standards**

Writing 3. Write narratives in which they recount a well-elaborated event or short sequence of events, include details to describe actions, thoughts, and feelings, use temporal words to signal event order, and provide a sense of closure.

Connect the Texts
Narrative Paragraph

Student Prompt Look back at *Henry and Mudge and the Starry Night.* Write a paragraph to describe Henry making s'mores over the campfire. Think about what Mudge might do to get the graham crackers. Describe what happens between the two characters.

_____

- -

_____

- -

_____

- -

_____

- -

_____

- -

_____

- -

_____

- -

_____

- -

_____

- -

_____

Connect the Texts
Narrative Paragraph

Student Prompt, p. 16 Look back at *Henry and Mudge and the Starry Night.* Write a paragraph to describe Henry making s'mores over the campfire. Think about what Mudge might do to get the graham crackers. Describe what happens between the two characters.

Writing to Sources Have children reread "How to Make a S'more." Tell them the photographs and captions will provide details that describe the process Henry will use. Remind children how Henry feels about Mudge. Suggest they include those feelings while describing how Mudge will react around the s'mores.

		4-point Narrative Writing Rubric			
Score	**Narrative Focus**	**Organization**	**Development of Narrative**	**Language and Vocabulary**	**Conventions**
4	Narrative is clearly focused and developed throughout.	Narrative has a well-developed, logical, easy-to-follow plot.	Narrative includes thorough and effective use of details, dialogue, and description.	Narrative uses precise, concrete sensory language as well as figurative language and/or domain-specific vocabulary.	Narrative has correct grammar, usage, spelling, capitalization, and punctuation.
3	Narrative is mostly focused and developed throughout.	Narrative has a plot, but there may be some lack of clarity and/or unrelated events.	Narrative includes adequate use of details, dialogue and description.	Narrative uses adequate sensory and figurative language and/or domain-specific vocabulary.	Narrative has a few errors but is completely understandable.
2	Narrative is somewhat developed but may occasionally lose focus.	Narrative's plot is difficult to follow, and ideas are not connected well.	Narrative includes only a few details, dialogues, and descriptions.	Language in narrative is not precise or sensory; lacks domain-specific vocabulary.	Narrative has some errors in usage, grammar, spelling and/or punctuation.
1	Narrative may be confusing, unfocused, or too short.	Narrative has little or no apparent plot.	Narrative includes few or no details, dialogue or description.	Language in narrative is vague, unclear, or confusing.	Narrative is hard to follow because of frequent errors.
0	Narrative gets no credit if it does not demonstrate adequate command of narrative writing traits.				

© Common Core State Standards

Writing 3. Write narratives in which they recount a well-elaborated event or short sequence of events, include details to describe actions, thoughts, and feelings, use temporal words to signal event order, and provide a sense of closure.

Name_____

Write Like a Reporter
Narrative Postcard

Student Prompt Reread pages 128–131 of *A Walk in the Desert*. Imagine you are on vacation in the desert. Write a postcard to a friend back home describing your experience. Refer to the descriptions in the selection to help you elaborate your text.

_____

_____

_____

_____

_____

_____

_____

_____

_____

_____

_____

_____

_____

_____

_____

_____

_____

_____

Write Like a Reporter
Narrative Postcard

> **Student Prompt, p. 18** Reread pages 128–131 of *A Walk in the Desert*. Imagine you are on vacation in the desert. Write a postcard to a friend back home describing your experience. Refer to the descriptions in the selection to help you elaborate your text.

Writing to Sources Explain to children that a good narration includes personal experience and sensory details. Use the facts and descriptions in the text to help create details that the children will use.

Children's writing should:

- provide a setting, narrator, and characters
- include a chronology of events that reflects those in the text
- use descriptive words and sensory details in the retelling of events
- demonstrate strong command of the conventions of standard written English

Writing 3. Write narratives in which they recount a well-elaborated event or short sequence of events, include details to describe actions, thoughts, and feelings, use temporal words to signal event order, and provide a sense of closure.

Name_____

Connect the Texts

Narrative Paragraph

Student Prompt Reread pages 128–135 of *A Walk in the Desert* and pp. 144–145 of "Rain Forests." Choose one of the desert animals and write a paragraph about his or her experiences on a vacation to the rain forest. Use details from both texts in your writing.

_____

_____

_____

_____

_____

_____

_____

_____

_____

_____

_____

_____

_____

_____

_____

_____

Connect the Texts
Narrative Paragraph

Student Prompt, p. 20 Reread pages 128–135 of *A Walk in the Desert* and pp. 144–145 of "Rain Forests." Choose one of the desert animals and write a paragraph about his or her experiences on a vacation to the rain forest. Use details from both texts in your writing.

Writing to Sources Have children review *A Walk in the Desert.* Point out that the photographs, labels, and details found in the text provide sensory details for the children's story. Explain that they will create events, or experiences, for their characters, and the setting will be in the rain forest.

			4-point Narrative Writing Rubric		
Score	**Narrative Focus**	**Organization**	**Development of Narrative**	**Language and Vocabulary**	**Conventions**
4	Narrative is clearly focused and developed throughout.	Narrative has a well-developed, logical, easy-to-follow plot.	Narrative includes thorough and effective use of details, dialogue, and description.	Narrative uses precise, concrete sensory language as well as figurative language and/or domain-specific vocabulary.	Narrative has correct grammar, usage, spelling, capitalization, and punctuation.
3	Narrative is mostly focused and developed throughout.	Narrative has a plot, but there may be some lack of clarity and/or unrelated events.	Narrative includes adequate use of details, dialogue and description.	Narrative uses adequate sensory and figurative language and/or domain-specific vocabulary.	Narrative has a few errors but is completely understandable.
2	Narrative is somewhat developed but may occasionally lose focus.	Narrative's plot is difficult to follow, and ideas are not connected well.	Narrative includes only a few details, dialogues, and descriptions.	Language in narrative is not precise or sensory; lacks domain-specific vocabulary.	Narrative has some errors in usage, grammar, spelling and/or punctuation.
1	Narrative may be confusing, unfocused, or too short.	Narrative has little or no apparent plot.	Narrative includes few or no details, dialogue or description.	Language in narrative is vague, unclear, or confusing.	Narrative is hard to follow because of frequent errors.
0	Narrative gets no credit if it does not demonstrate adequate command of narrative writing traits.				

Ⓒ **Common Core State Standards**

Writing 3. Write narratives in which they recount a well-elaborated event or short sequence of events, include details to describe actions, thoughts, and feelings, use temporal words to signal event order, and provide a sense of closure.

Name_____

Write Like a Reporter
Narrative Scene

Student Prompt Look back through *The Strongest One* and see how the author uses dialogue to write the play. Write another scene in which Little Red Ant meets a new character.

_____
- -
_____
- -
_____
- -
_____
- -
_____
- -
_____
- -
_____
- -
_____
- -
_____
- -
_____
- -
_____
- -
_____

Write Like a Reporter
Narrative Scene

Student Prompt, p. 22 Look back through *The Strongest One* and see how the author uses dialogue to write the play. Write another scene in which Little Red Ant meets a new character.

Writing to Sources Discuss with children that this is a fantasy that takes place in the desert. Explain that animals and things can speak in a fantasy. Remind children of the animals in *A Walk in the Desert* to assist them in developing a new character for the play.

Children's scenes should:

- provide a setting, narrator, and/or characters
- have focus and include events that are true to those in the text
- use details and descriptive words that identify the plot
- demonstrate strong command of the conventions of standard written English

© **Common Core State Standards**

Writing 3. Write narratives in which they recount a well-elaborated event or short sequence of events, include details to describe actions, thoughts, and feelings, use temporal words to signal event order, and provide a sense of closure.

Name_____

Connect the Texts
Narrative Paragraph

Student Prompt Describe an incident where Little Red Ant meets an anteater for the first time. Use sensory words and details from "Anteaters" and *The Strongest One* to help describe Little Red Ant's personal experience.

_____
- -
_____
- -
_____
- -
_____
- -
_____
- -
_____
- -
_____
- -
_____
- -
_____
- -
_____

Connect the Texts

Narrative Paragraph

Student Prompt, p. 24 Describe an incident where Little Red Ant meets an anteater for the first time. Use sensory words and details from "Anteaters" and *The Strongest One* to help describe Little Red Ant's personal experience.

Writing to Sources Discuss with children how Little Red Ant may feel as he meets an anteater. Tell them he may want to run away or he may ask for information on how to keep his home safe. Explain to children that how Little Red Ant feels about the anteater will influence how Little Red Ant responds to the character. Look for the descriptive images in "Anteaters" to inspire children's thoughts about Little Red Ant's response.

			4-point Narrative Writing Rubric		
Score	**Narrative Focus**	**Organization**	**Development of Narrative**	**Language and Vocabulary**	**Conventions**
4	Narrative is clearly focused and developed throughout.	Narrative has a well-developed, logical, easy-to-follow plot.	Narrative includes thorough and effective use of details, dialogue, and description.	Narrative uses precise, concrete sensory language as well as figurative language and/or domain-specific vocabulary.	Narrative has correct grammar, usage, spelling, capitalization, and punctuation.
3	Narrative is mostly focused and developed throughout.	Narrative has a plot, but there may be some lack of clarity and/or unrelated events.	Narrative includes adequate use of details, dialogue and description.	Narrative uses adequate sensory and figurative language and/or domain-specific vocabulary.	Narrative has a few errors but is completely understandable.
2	Narrative is somewhat developed but may occasionally lose focus.	Narrative's plot is difficult to follow, and ideas are not connected well.	Narrative includes only a few details, dialogues, and descriptions.	Language in narrative is not precise or sensory; lacks domain-specific vocabulary.	Narrative has some errors in usage, grammar, spelling and/or punctuation.
1	Narrative may be confusing, unfocused, or too short.	Narrative has little or no apparent plot.	Narrative includes few or no details, dialogue or description.	Language in narrative is vague, unclear, or confusing.	Narrative is hard to follow because of frequent errors.
0	Narrative gets no credit if it does not demonstrate adequate command of narrative writing traits.				

© Common Core State Standards

Writing 3. Write narratives in which they recount a well-elaborated event or short sequence of events, include details to describe actions, thoughts, and feelings, use temporal words to signal event order, and provide a sense of closure.

Prove It!
Play Scene

ELL

Introduce Genre Write *play* and *drama* on the board and explain that these words describe a story written to be performed by actors on a stage. Explain that the story is told by actors using stage directions and dialogue, or words written for them to speak. Discuss with children the key features of a play or drama that appear on this page.

Exploring the Desert

Play Scene

In this unit, children have read examples of narrative writing, including a play or drama and two stories, and have had the opportunity to write in this mode. Remind children of texts and writing tasks (such as Write Like a Reporter and Connect the Texts) in which they have encountered and practiced narrative writing. Also review how the format of a play differs from the format of a story.

Key Features of a Play or Drama
- has characters, a setting, and a plot
- includes brief stage directions describing the scene and action
- primarily uses dialogue to tell a story
- has a beginning, middle, and end
- uses punctuation and formatting to differentiate stage directions from dialogue

Writing Task Overview

Each unit writing task provides children with an opportunity to write to sources. To successfully complete the task, children must analyze, synthesize, and evaluate multiple complex texts and create their own written response.

Exploring the Desert
Part 1: Children will reread the selections identified from this unit. They will then respond to questions about these sources and discuss their written responses with partners.

Part 2: Children will work individually to plan, write, and revise their own play scene.

Scorable Products: evidence-based short responses, play scene

Exploring the Desert: Writing Task – Short Response

Teacher Directions:

1. Introduce the Sources Refer children to the following texts in the Student Edition:

1. *A Walk in the Desert* pp. 120–139

2. *The Strongest One* pp. 156–173

Explain to children that they will need to find information in these texts to answer questions. Tell children that they will also write their own play scenes using information from the texts.

2. Provide Student Directions (pp. 30–31) Answer any task-related questions children may have.

3. Facilitate Collaboration After children have completed their written responses to the evidence-based short response questions, assign partners or small groups and have them discuss their responses. If children struggle to work together productively, provide them with tips and strategies for expressing their ideas and building on others'.

© **Common Core State Standards**

Writing 3. Write narratives in which they recount a well-elaborated event or short sequence of events, include details to describe actions, thoughts, and feelings, use temporal words to signal event order, and provide a sense of closure.

Scoring Information

Use the following 2-point scoring rubrics to evaluate children's answers to the evidence-based short response questions.

1. What can you infer about Little Red Ant from what he says and does in *The Strongest One?* Cite examples from the text.

Analysis Rubric	
2	The response: • demonstrates the ability to analyze characterization in a story • includes specific details that make reference to the text
1	The response: • demonstrates a limited ability to analyze characterization in a story • includes some details that make reference to the text
0	A response receives no credit if it demonstrates no ability to analyze characterization in a story or includes no relevant details from the text.

2. Based on *A Walk in the Desert,* what animals might Little Red Ant meet if he explored the desert? How do you think he would react to each animal?

	Synthesis Rubric
2	The response: • demonstrates the ability to synthesize information from the sources in order to describe how a known character would react to new characters in a new setting • includes specific details that make reference to the texts
1	The response: • demonstrates a limited ability to synthesize information from the sources in order to describe how a known character would react to new characters in a new setting • includes some details that make reference to the texts
0	A response receives no credit if it demonstrates no ability to synthesize information from the sources or includes no relevant details from the texts.

© **Common Core State Standards**

Writing 3. Write narratives in which they recount a well-elaborated event or short sequence of events, include details to describe actions, thoughts, and feelings, use temporal words to signal event order, and provide a sense of closure.

Name _____

Exploring the Desert
Writing Task – Short Response

I. What can you infer about Little Red Ant from what he says and does in *The Strongest One?* Cite examples from the text.

_____

- -

_____

- -

_____

- -

_____

- -

_____

- -

_____

- -

_____

- -

_____

- -

_____

- -

_____

- -

_____

Name _____

2. Based on *A Walk in the Desert*, what animals might Little Red Ant meet if he explored the desert? How do you think he would react to each animal?

_____

- -

_____

- -

_____

- -

_____

- -

_____

- -

_____

- -

_____

- -

_____

- -

_____

- -

_____

Exploring the Desert: Writing Task – Play Scene

Teacher Directions:

1. **Provide Directions (p. 34)** Explain to children that they will now review the sources and plan, draft, and revise their play scenes. Children will be allowed to look back at the answers they wrote to the short response questions. Read aloud the directions for the play scene and answer any task-related questions they may have. Children should be given paper on which to write their play scenes.

2. **Scoring Information** Use the scoring rubric on the next page to evaluate children's play scenes.

3. **Play Scene Prompt** Write a scene for a play in which Little Red Ant from *The Strongest One* explores the desert in *A Walk in the Desert*. He meets desert animals and learns a lesson about life in the desert. Use a scene in *The Strongest One* as a model.

Narrative Writing Rubric					
Score	Narrative Focus	Organization	Development of Narrative	Language and Vocabulary	Conventions
4	Play scene is strongly focused throughout.	Play scene has a well-developed plot.	Play scene includes effective use of details and dialogue.	Play scene uses precise, concrete sensory language.	Play scene has correct grammar, usage, spelling, capitalization, and punctuation.
3	Play scene is mostly focused throughout.	Play scene has a plot with some unrelated events.	Play scene includes adequate use of details and dialogue.	Play scene uses adequate sensory language.	Play scene has a few errors but is understandable.
2	Play scene is somewhat focused.	Play scene's plot is not clear.	Play scene includes only a few details and some dialogue.	Play scene's language is not precise or sensory.	Play scene has some errors in usage, grammar, spelling, and/or punctuation.
1	Play scene is confusing.	Play scene has little or no plot.	Play scene includes few or no details or dialogue.	Play scene's language is vague or confusing.	Play scene is hard to follow because of numerous errors.
0	Play scene receives no credit if it does not demonstrate adequate command of narrative writing traits.				

Common Core State Standards

Writing 3. Write narratives in which they recount a well-elaborated event or short sequence of events, include details to describe actions, thoughts, and feelings, use temporal words to signal event order, and provide a sense of closure.

Exploring the Desert

Writing Task – Play Scene

Play Scene Prompt

Write a scene for a play in which Little Red Ant from *The Strongest One* explores the desert in *A Walk in the Desert.*

What animals does Little Red Ant meet?

_____

_____

What do the animals tell Little Red Ant about life in the desert?

_____

_____

_____

_____

What lesson does Little Red Ant learn?

_____

_____

_____

_____

How can the play *The Strongest One* help you write your scene?

_____

_____

_____

_____

Exploring the Desert: Writing Task – Play Scene

Teacher Directions:

1. Publish Explain to children that publishing their writing is the last step in the writing process. If time permits, have children review one another's compositions and incorporate any comments their classmates have. Discuss different ways technology can be used to publish writing.

2. Present Children will now have the option to present their play scenes. Have children share parts with a partner and read aloud their play scenes in front of the class. Use the list below to offer children tips on listening and speaking.

While Listening to a Classmate...
- Face the speaker to listen attentively.
- Take notes on what the speaker says.

While Speaking to Classmates...
- Determine your purpose for speaking.
- Have good posture and eye contact.
- Use expression to show appropriate mood.

Things to Do Together...
- Ask and answer questions with detail.
- Build on each other's ideas.

Writing 3. Write narratives in which they recount a well-elaborated event or short sequence of events, include details to describe actions, thoughts, and feelings, use temporal words to signal event order, and provide a sense of closure.

Unit 2 Working Together

Writing Focus: Informative/Explanatory

Write Like a Reporter

Explanatory Steps

Student Prompt Reread pages 200–204 of *Tara and Tiree, Fearless Friends.* How did the dogs save Jim's life? Write the sequence of events as a set of steps in a process. Use details from the text to tell about each step. Add time-order words to clarify the sequence.

Write Like a Reporter

Informative/Explanatory
Steps in a Process

Student Prompt, p. 38 Reread pages 200–204 of *Tara and Tiree, Fearless Friends.* How did the dogs save Jim's life? Write the sequence of events as a set of steps in a process. Use details from the text to tell about each step. Add time-order words to clarify the sequence.

Writing to Sources Discuss with children what the dogs do to rescue Jim. Emphasize that these events happen in a specific order, or sequence, just like the steps in a process. Suggest that children first identify and write the sequence of events involved in the rescue and then organize the events as steps using time-order words and action verbs.

Children's writing should:

- include time-order words and/or numbers
- include some facts and details about each step
- provide a chronological order of steps or events
- demonstrate strong command of the conventions of standard written English

© **Common Core State Standards**

Writing 2. Write informative/explanatory texts in which they introduce a topic, use facts and definitions to develop points, and provide a concluding statement or section.

Connect the Texts

Explanatory Paragraph

Student Prompt Write a paragraph comparing and contrasting the dogs in *Tara and Tiree, Fearless Friends* and the dogs in "Rescue Dogs." Are all the dogs smart? Are they strong? Use evidence from the texts to support your ideas.

_____

_____

_____

_____

_____

_____

_____

_____

_____

_____

_____

_____

_____

_____

_____

Connect the Texts
Informative/Explanatory Compare and Contrast Paragraph

Student Prompt, p. 40 Write a paragraph comparing and contrasting the dogs in *Tara and Tiree, Fearless Friends* and the dogs in "Rescue Dogs." Are all the dogs smart? Are they strong? Use evidence from the texts to support your ideas.

Writing to Sources Review the events in both selections with children. Ask them to think of adjectives they would use to describe Tara and Tiree and adjectives they would use to describe the rescue dogs. Ask children to identify which adjectives all the dogs have in common. Once children have chosen one or two characteristics as their focus, ask them to look for evidence in the texts that supports their ideas.

	Informative/Explanatory Writing Rubric				
Score	**Focus**	**Organization**	**Development of Evidence**	**Language and Vocabulary**	**Conventions**
4	Main idea is clearly conveyed and well supported; response is focused.	Organization is clear and effective, creating a sense of cohesion.	Evidence is relevant and thorough; includes facts and details.	Ideas are clearly and effectively conveyed, using precise language and/or domain-specific vocabulary.	Command of conventions is strongly demonstrated.
3	Main idea is clear, adequately supported; response is generally focused.	Organization is clear, though minor flaws may be present and some ideas may be disconnected.	Evidence is adequate and includes facts and details.	Ideas are adequately conveyed, using both precise and more general language; may include domain-specific vocabulary.	Command of conventions is sufficiently demonstrated.
2	Main idea is somewhat supported; lacks focus or includes unnecessary material.	Organization is inconsistent, and flaws are apparent.	Evidence is uneven or incomplete; insufficient use of facts and details.	Ideas are unevenly conveyed, using overly-simplistic language; lacks domain-specific vocabulary.	Command of conventions is uneven.
1	Response may be confusing, unfocused; main idea insufficiently supported.	Organization is poor or nonexistent.	Evidence is poor or nonexistent.	Ideas are conveyed in a vague, unclear, or confusing manner.	There is very little command of conventions.
0	The response shows no evidence of the ability to construct a coherent explanatory essay using information from sources.				

Ⓒ Common Core State Standards

Writing 2. Write informative/explanatory texts in which they introduce a topic, use facts and definitions to develop points, and provide a concluding statement or section.

Write Like a Reporter

Explanatory Paragraph

Student Prompt Review pages 230–237 of *Abraham Lincoln.* What do the details of Abraham Lincoln's life suggest about his character? Choose three important events from Lincoln's life. Write a paragraph explaining these events and how they tell why many people call Lincoln "America's Great President." Use evidence to support your conclusions.

_____

_____

_____

_____

_____

_____

_____

_____

_____

_____

_____

_____

_____

_____

_____

_____

Write Like a Reporter

Informative/Explanatory Paragraph

Student Prompt, p. 42 Review pages 230–237 of *Abraham Lincoln*. What do the details of Abraham Lincoln's life suggest about his character? Choose three important events from Lincoln's life. Write a paragraph explaining these events and how they tell why many people call Lincoln "America's Great President." Use evidence to support your conclusions.

Writing to Sources As you revisit the selection with children, create a list of major events from Lincoln's life. Have children choose three events and add details to support their writing. When they have finished writing, invite children to share the three events they selected.

Children's paragraphs should:

- introduce a topic or text
- supply some facts and details about the topic
- use text evidence to support conclusions
- demonstrate strong command of the conventions of standard written English

Ⓒ **Common Core State Standards**

Writing 2. Write informative/explanatory texts in which they introduce a topic, use facts and definitions to develop points, and provide a concluding statement or section.

Connect the Texts
Explanatory Paragraph

Student Prompt Review the selection *Abraham Lincoln.* Then reread the final stanza of the poem "Lincoln." Do the details of *Abraham Lincoln* support the feelings in this stanza? Write a paragraph that compares the two selections. Use precise words and evidence from the texts to support your ideas.

_____

_____

_____

_____

_____

_____

_____

_____

_____

_____

_____

_____

_____

_____

_____

_____

_____

Connect the Texts
Informative/Explanatory Paragraph

Student Prompt, p. 44 Review the selection *Abraham Lincoln*. Then reread the final stanza of the poem "Lincoln." Do the details of *Abraham Lincoln* support the feelings in this stanza? Write a paragraph that compares the two selections. Use precise words and evidence from the texts to support your ideas.

Writing to Sources Review the ideas in *Abraham Lincoln*. Look back at "Lincoln" and clarify any parts of the poem that may confuse children. Suggest that, as children revisit the poem, they ask themselves how each line compares to a certain event or idea from *Abraham Lincoln*. Remind them to support their paragraphs with evidence and precise words.

	Informative/Explanatory Writing Rubric				
Score	**Focus**	**Organization**	**Development of Evidence**	**Language and Vocabulary**	**Conventions**
4	Main idea is clearly conveyed and well supported; response is focused.	Organization is clear and effective, creating a sense of cohesion.	Evidence is relevant and thorough; includes facts and details.	Ideas are clearly and effectively conveyed, using precise language and/or domain-specific vocabulary.	Command of conventions is strongly demonstrated.
3	Main idea is clear, adequately supported; response is generally focused.	Organization is clear, though minor flaws may be present and some ideas may be disconnected.	Evidence is adequate and includes facts and details.	Ideas are adequately conveyed, using both precise and more general language; may include domain-specific vocabulary.	Command of conventions is sufficiently demonstrated.
2	Main idea is somewhat supported; lacks focus or includes unnecessary material.	Organization is inconsistent, and flaws are apparent.	Evidence is uneven or incomplete; insufficient use of facts and details.	Ideas are unevenly conveyed, using overly-simplistic language; lacks domain-specific vocabulary.	Command of conventions is uneven.
1	Response may be confusing, unfocused; main idea insufficiently supported.	Organization is poor or nonexistent.	Evidence is poor or nonexistent.	Ideas are conveyed in a vague, unclear, or confusing manner.	There is very little command of conventions.
0	The response shows no evidence of the ability to construct a coherent explanatory essay using information from sources.				

© Common Core State Standards

Writing 2. Write informative/explanatory texts in which they introduce a topic, use facts and definitions to develop points, and provide a concluding statement or section.

Write Like a Reporter

Explanatory Paragraph

Student Prompt Reread pages 260–261 of *Scarcity*. Why isn't the company selling juice? Write a paragraph explaining the company's decision. Provide evidence from the text to support your explanation.

_____

- -

_____

_____

- -

_____

_____

- -

_____

_____

- -

_____

_____

- -

_____

_____

- -

_____

_____

- -

_____

_____

- -

_____

Write Like a Reporter
Informative/Explanatory Paragraph

Student Prompt, p. 46 Reread pages 260–261 of *Scarcity*. Why isn't the company selling juice? Write a paragraph explaining the company's decision. Provide evidence from the text to support your explanation.

Writing to Sources As children look back at the text, encourage them to read carefully and look for evidence to support their writing. Suggest that they use time-order words to help the flow of their explanations.

Children's paragraphs should:

- introduce a topic
- use text evidence
- include time-order words for sequence clarification
- demonstrate strong command of the conventions of standard written English

---

Ⓒ **Common Core State Standards**

Writing 2. Write informative/explanatory texts in which they introduce a topic, use facts and definitions to develop points, and provide a concluding statement or section.

Connect the Texts

Explanatory Paragraph

> **Student Prompt** Review *Scarcity* and "Goods and Services." Jordan uses the Internet to research economics. Use his chosen Web site to write an explanation of the word *scarcity.* Use vocabulary from each selection to write your paragraphs.

_____

_____

_____

_____

_____

_____

_____

_____

_____

_____

_____

_____

_____

_____

_____

_____

_____

_____

_____

_____

Connect the Texts

Informative/Explanatory Paragraph

Student Prompt, p. 48 Review *Scarcity* and "Goods and Services." Jordan uses the Internet to research economics. Use his chosen Web site to write an explanation of the word *scarcity.* Use vocabulary from each selection to write your paragraphs.

Writing to Sources Have children review both selections. Ask them to scan *Scarcity* and identify places where they could replace a word or a phrase with the word *good* or *service.* Once children comprehend how the two selections are connected, allow them to choose a good or service of their liking to explain scarcity.

			Informative/Explanatory Writing Rubric		
Score	**Focus**	**Organization**	**Development of Evidence**	**Language and Vocabulary**	**Conventions**
4	Main idea is clearly conveyed and well supported; response is focused.	Organization is clear and effective, creating a sense of cohesion.	Evidence is relevant and thorough; includes facts and details.	Ideas are clearly and effectively conveyed, using precise language and/or domain-specific vocabulary.	Command of conventions is strongly demonstrated.
3	Main idea is clear, adequately supported; response is generally focused.	Organization is clear, though minor flaws may be present and some ideas may be disconnected.	Evidence is adequate and includes facts and details.	Ideas are adequately conveyed, using both precise and more general language; may include domain-specific vocabulary.	Command of conventions is sufficiently demonstrated.
2	Main idea is somewhat supported; lacks focus or includes unnecessary material.	Organization is inconsistent, and flaws are apparent.	Evidence is uneven or incomplete; insufficient use of facts and details.	Ideas are unevenly conveyed, using overly-simplistic language; lacks domain-specific vocabulary.	Command of conventions is uneven.
1	Response may be confusing, unfocused; main idea insufficiently supported.	Organization is poor or nonexistent.	Evidence is poor or nonexistent.	Ideas are conveyed in a vague, unclear, or confusing manner.	There is very little command of conventions.
0	The response shows no evidence of the ability to construct a coherent explanatory essay using information from sources.				

Ⓒ Common Core State Standards

Writing 2. Write informative/explanatory texts in which they introduce a topic, use facts and definitions to develop points, and provide a concluding statement or section.

Name_____

Write Like a Reporter
Explanatory Summary

> **Student Prompt** Imagine a classmate is summarizing *The Bremen Town Musicians.* The classmate claims the robbers and the musicians all ran from the house because they were frightened by monsters. What is wrong with this statement? How would you correctly summarize the end of the play?

_____

- -

_____

- -

_____

- -

_____

- -

_____

- -

_____

- -

_____

- -

_____

- -

_____

- -

Write Like a Reporter

Informative/Explanatory Summary

Student Prompt, p. 50 Imagine a classmate is summarizing *The Bremen Town Musicians.* The classmate claims the robbers and the musicians all ran from the house because they were frightened by monsters. What is wrong with this statement? How would you correctly summarize the end of the play?

Writing to Sources Emphasize that the robbers ran from the house twice. Discuss the sequence of events that led to the musicians' first encounter with the robbers. Then have them prepare their summaries of the play's ending. Suggest that children organize events as steps using time-order words and action verbs.

Children's paragraphs should:

- introduce a topic
- supply some facts and details about the topic
- summarize using time-order words and action verbs
- demonstrate strong command of the conventions of standard written English

Ⓒ **Common Core State Standards**

Writing 2. Write informative/explanatory texts in which they introduce a topic, use facts and definitions to develop points, and provide a concluding statement or section.

Name_____

Connect the Texts

Explanatory Paragraph

Student Prompt Write a paragraph focusing on the use of trickery in *The Bremen Town Musicians* and in "A Fool Goes Fishing." Who is trying to trick whom? Do the tricks work? Use evidence from the texts for support.

_____

_____

_____

_____

_____

_____

_____

_____

_____

_____

_____

_____

_____

_____

_____

_____

_____

_____

Connect the Texts

Informative/Explanatory Paragraph

Student Prompt, p. 52 Write a paragraph focusing on the use of trickery in *The Bremen Town Musicians* and in "A Fool Goes Fishing." Who is trying to trick whom? Do the tricks work? Use evidence from the texts for support.

Writing to Sources Tell children that fables and folk tales often involve a sneaky character, or a prankster. Review the events in both selections with children. Who are the pranksters in each tale? Remind children to focus on the use of trickery and ask them to support their explanations with evidence.

			Informative/Explanatory Writing Rubric		
Score	**Focus**	**Organization**	**Development of Evidence**	**Language and Vocabulary**	**Conventions**
4	Main idea is clearly conveyed and well supported; response is focused.	Organization is clear and effective, creating a sense of cohesion.	Evidence is relevant and thorough; includes facts and details.	Ideas are clearly and effectively conveyed, using precise language and/or domain-specific vocabulary.	Command of conventions is strongly demonstrated.
3	Main idea is clear, adequately supported; response is generally focused.	Organization is clear, though minor flaws may be present and some ideas may be disconnected.	Evidence is adequate and includes facts and details.	Ideas are adequately conveyed, using both precise and more general language; may include domain-specific vocabulary.	Command of conventions is sufficiently demonstrated.
2	Main idea is somewhat supported; lacks focus or includes unnecessary material.	Organization is inconsistent, and flaws are apparent.	Evidence is uneven or incomplete; insufficient use of facts and details.	Ideas are unevenly conveyed, using overly-simplistic language; lacks domain-specific vocabulary.	Command of conventions is uneven.
1	Response may be confusing, unfocused; main idea insufficiently supported.	Organization is poor or nonexistent.	Evidence is poor or nonexistent.	Ideas are conveyed in a vague, unclear, or confusing manner.	There is very little command of conventions.
0	The response shows no evidence of the ability to construct a coherent explanatory essay using information from sources.				

© Common Core State Standards

Writing 2. Write informative/explanatory texts in which they introduce a topic, use facts and definitions to develop points, and provide a concluding statement or section.

Name_____

Write Like a Reporter

Explanatory Paragraph

Student Prompt Reread pages 334–335 of *One Good Turn Deserves Another.* What does the coyote mean by "one good turn"? Use evidence from the text to support your answer.

_____
- -
_____
- -
_____
- -
_____
- -
_____
- -
_____
- -
_____
- -
_____
- -
_____
- -
_____
- -
_____

Write Like a Reporter
Informative/Explanatory Paragraph

> **Student Prompt, p. 54** Reread pages 334–335 of *One Good Turn Deserves Another.* What does the coyote mean by "one good turn"? Use evidence from the text to support your answer.

Writing to Sources Ask volunteers to share a situation in which someone did something nice for them. Did they do something nice to repay the favor? Use this scenario to define the word "deserve." Then have children prepare their responses, using evidence from the text for support.

Children's paragraphs should:

- introduce a topic
- supply some facts and details about the topic
- use evidence for support, including precise words
- demonstrate strong command of the conventions of standard written English

ⓒ Common Core State Standards

Writing 2. Write informative/explanatory texts in which they introduce a topic, use facts and definitions to develop points, and provide a concluding statement or section.

Connect the Texts

Explanatory Comparison

Student Prompt Identify the lessons, or morals, of *One Good Turn Deserves Another* and "The Lion and the Mouse." Write a paragraph comparing and contrasting the lessons these stories teach. Use evidence from the texts to support your ideas.

_____

_____

_____

_____

_____

_____

_____

_____

_____

_____

_____

_____

Connect the Texts

Informative/Explanatory Compare and Contrast Paragraph

Student Prompt, p. 56 Identify the lessons, or morals, of *One Good Turn Deserves Another* and "The Lion and the Mouse." Write a paragraph comparing and contrasting the lessons these stories teach. Use evidence from the texts to support your ideas.

Writing to Sources Discuss with children that folk tales often teach a lesson, or a moral. Help children identify the morals in *One Good Turn Deserves Another* and "The Lion and the Mouse." Suggest that they ask themselves questions to compare and contrast the selections. As they write, remind children to remain focused and to use evidence to support their writing.

			Informative/Explanatory Writing Rubric		
Score	**Focus**	**Organization**	**Development of Evidence**	**Language and Vocabulary**	**Conventions**
4	Main idea is clearly conveyed and well supported; response is focused.	Organization is clear and effective, creating a sense of cohesion.	Evidence is relevant and thorough; includes facts and details.	Ideas are clearly and effectively conveyed, using precise language and/or domain-specific vocabulary.	Command of conventions is strongly demonstrated.
3	Main idea is clear, adequately supported; response is generally focused.	Organization is clear, though minor flaws may be present and some ideas may be disconnected.	Evidence is adequate and includes facts and details.	Ideas are adequately conveyed, using both precise and more general language; may include domain-specific vocabulary.	Command of conventions is sufficiently demonstrated.
2	Main idea is somewhat supported; lacks focus or includes unnecessary material.	Organization is inconsistent, and flaws are apparent.	Evidence is uneven or incomplete; insufficient use of facts and details.	Ideas are unevenly conveyed, using overly-simplistic language; lacks domain-specific vocabulary.	Command of conventions is uneven.
1	Response may be confusing, unfocused; main idea insufficiently supported.	Organization is poor or nonexistent.	Evidence is poor or nonexistent.	Ideas are conveyed in a vague, unclear, or confusing manner.	There is very little command of conventions.
0	The response shows no evidence of the ability to construct a coherent explanatory essay using information from sources.				

Ⓒ **Common Core State Standards**

Writing 2. Write informative/explanatory texts in which they introduce a topic, use facts and definitions to develop points, and provide a concluding statement or section.

Prove It!
Compare and Contrast Essay

Stronger Together

Compare and Contrast Essay

In this unit, children have read examples of informative/explanatory writing, including informative articles and literary nonfiction, and have had the opportunity to write in this mode. Remind children of texts and writing tasks (such as Write Like a Reporter and Connect the Texts) in which they have encountered and practiced informative/explanatory writing.

Key Features of a Compare and Contrast Essay

- points out ways two or more subjects are alike and different
- organizes ideas by subject or by feature compared or contrasted
- includes supporting details to illustrate similarities or differences
- uses words such as *like, both, similarly* to indicate similarities and *unlike, but, however* to indicate differences
- provides a concluding statement or section related to the topic

Writing Task Overview

Each unit writing task provides children with an opportunity to write to sources. To successfully complete the task, children must analyze, synthesize, and evaluate multiple complex texts and create their own written response.

Stronger Together

Part 1: Children will reread the selections identified from this unit. They will then respond to questions about these sources and discuss their written responses with partners.

Part 2: Children will work individually to plan, write, and revise their own compare and contrast essay.

Scorable Products: evidence-based short responses, compare and contrast essay

Stronger Together: Writing Task – Short Response

Teacher Directions:

1. Introduce the Sources Refer children to the following texts in the Student Edition:

1. *Tara and Tiree: Fearless Friends* pp. 192–207

2. *The Bremen Town Musicians* pp. 284–301

Explain to children that they will need to find information in these texts to answer questions. Tell children that they will also write their own compare and contrast essays using information from the texts.

2. Provide Directions (pp. 62–63) Answer any task-related questions children may have.

3. Facilitate Collaboration After children have completed their written responses to the evidence-based short response questions, assign partners or small groups and have them discuss their responses. If children struggle to work together productively, provide them with tips and strategies for expressing their ideas and building on others'.

© Common Core State Standards

Writing 2. Write informative/explanatory texts in which they introduce a topic, use facts and definitions to develop points, and provide a concluding statement or section.

Scoring Information

Use the following 2-point scoring rubrics to evaluate children's answers to the evidence-based short response questions.

1. Who works together in the stories and what do they accomplish, or get done?

	Analysis Rubric
2	The response: • demonstrates the ability to identify characters working as a team and analyze their achievements that are described in the texts • includes specific details that make reference to the texts
1	The response: • demonstrates a limited ability to identify characters working as a team and analyze their achievements that are described in the texts • includes some details that make reference to the texts
0	A response receives no credit if it demonstrates no ability to identify characters working as a team and analyze their achievements or includes no relevant details from the texts.

2. Why do the characters in each selection decide to work together?

	Synthesis Rubric	
2	The response: • demonstrates the ability to synthesize information from the sources in order to explain motivation and degree of determination • includes specific details that make reference to the texts	
1	The response: • demonstrates a limited ability to synthesize information from the sources in order to explain motivation and degree of determination • includes some details that make reference to the texts	
0	A response receives no credit if it demonstrates no ability to synthesize information from the sources or includes no relevant details from the texts.	

© **Common Core State Standards**

Writing 2. Write informative/explanatory texts in which they introduce a topic, use facts and definitions to develop points, and provide a concluding statement or section.

Stronger Together

Writing Task – Short Response

1. Who works together in the stories and what do they accomplish, or get done?

_____

_____

_____

_____

_____

_____

_____

_____

_____

_____

_____

_____

_____

_____

_____

_____

2. Why do the characters in each selection decide to work together?

_____

_____

_____

_____

_____

_____

_____

_____

_____

_____

_____

_____

_____

_____

_____

_____

_____

_____

_____

_____

_____

_____

_____

_____

Stronger Together: Writing Task – Compare and Contrast Essay

Teacher Directions:

1. **Provide Directions (p. 66)** Explain to children that they will now review the sources and plan, draft, and revise their compare and contrast essays. Children will be allowed to look back at the answers they wrote for the short response questions. Read aloud the directions for the compare and contrast essay and answer any task-related questions they may have. Children should be given paper on which to write their compare and contrast essay.

2. **Scoring Information** Use the scoring rubric on the next page to evaluate children's compare and contrast essays.

3. **Compare and Contrast Essay Prompt** Write a compare and contrast essay about *Tara and Tiree: Fearless Friends* and *The Bremen Town Musicians.*

   How are the characters alike and different?

   How are their goals alike and different?

   What are the themes of the stories? Are they similar?

Informative/Explanatory Writing Rubric

Score	Focus	Organization	Development of Evidence	Language and Vocabulary	Conventions
4	Essay's topic is clearly stated and well supported with evidence.	Essay's organization includes an introduction, body, and conclusion.	Essay's evidence is thorough and carefully presented.	Essay uses precise language to present ideas effectively.	Essay has correct grammar, usage, spelling, capitalization, and punctuation.
3	Essay's topic is stated and adequately supported with evidence.	Essay's organization is clear, but some ideas are not well connected.	Essay's evidence is adequate.	Essay uses more general language to convey ideas adequately.	Essay has a few errors but is understandable.
2	Essay's topic is stated but lacks sufficient support.	Essay's organization is inconsistent.	Essay's evidence is incomplete or insufficient.	Essay uses overly simple language; ideas are not clearly stated.	Essay has some errors in usage, grammar, spelling, and/or punctuation.
1	Essay's topic is unclear and insufficiently supported.	Essay lacks organization.	Essay lacks sufficient evidence.	Essay's ideas are unclear or confusing.	Essay is hard to follow because of numerous errors.
0	Compare and contrast essay receives no credit if it does not demonstrate adequate command of informative/explanatory writing traits.				

Ⓒ Common Core State Standards

Writing 2. Write informative/explanatory texts in which they introduce a topic, use facts and definitions to develop points, and provide a concluding statement or section.

Name _____

Writing Task – Compare and Contrast Essay

Compare and Contrast Essay Prompt

Write a compare and contrast essay about *Tara and Tiree: Fearless Friends* and *The Bremen Town Musicians.*

How are the characters alike and different?

_____

_____

_____

_____

_____

How are their goals alike and different?

_____

_____

_____

_____

What are the themes of the stories? Are they similar?

_____

_____

_____

_____

Stronger Together: Writing Task – Compare and Contrast Essay

Teacher Directions:

1. Publish Explain to children that publishing their writing is the last step in the writing process. If time permits, have children review one another's compositions and incorporate any comments their classmates have. Discuss different ways technology can be used to publish writing.

2. Present Children will now have the option to present their compare and contrast essays. Have children read their essays aloud to one another in small groups. Use the list below to offer children tips on listening and speaking.

While Listening to a Classmate...

- Face the speaker to listen attentively.
- Take notes on what the speaker says.

While Speaking to Classmates...

- Determine your purpose for speaking.
- Have good posture and eye contact.
- Speak at an appropriate pace.

Things to Do Together...

- Ask and answer questions with detail.
- Build on each other's ideas.

Ⓒ **Common Core State Standards**

Writing 2. Write informative/explanatory texts in which they introduce a topic, use facts and definitions to develop points, and provide a concluding statement or section.

Unit 3 Creative Ideas

Writing Focus: Argument

Name_____

Write Like a Reporter
Argument: Paragraph

Student Prompt Reread *Pearl and Wagner: Two Good Friends.* Do you think Wagner is a good friend to Pearl? Write your opinion. Give reasons for your opinion, using evidence from the text as support.

_____

_____

_____

_____

_____

_____

_____

_____

_____

_____

_____

_____

_____

_____

Write Like a Reporter
Argumentative Paragraph

> **Student Prompt, p. 70** Reread *Pearl and Wagner: Two Good Friends.* Do you think Wagner is a good friend to Pearl? Write your opinion. Give reasons for your opinion, using evidence from the text as support.

Writing to Sources Explain to children that they should look for clues in the words and pictures in the text that will help them form an opinion about Wagner as a friend. Point out that the pictures on pages 356–359 are particularly helpful. Discuss children's opinions of Wagner and ask them what reasons they have for those opinions.

Children's paragraphs should:

- state a clear opinion about the topic
- supply reasons to support the opinion
- use evidence and facts from the text to support their reasons
- demonstrate strong command of the conventions of standard written English

Ⓒ Common Core State Standards

Writing 1. Write opinion pieces in which they introduce the topic or book they are writing about, state an opinion, supply reasons that support the opinion, use linking words (e.g., because, and, also) to connect opinion and reasons, and provide a concluding statement or section.

Connect the Texts

Argument: Paragraph

Student Prompt Reread *Pearl and Wagner: Two Good Friends* and "Alberto, the Scientist." Who do you think are the more successful scientists, Pearl and Wagner or Alberto? Write a paragraph that states your opinion and gives evidence from the text to support it.

_____

_____

_____

_____

_____

_____

_____

_____

_____

_____

_____

_____

_____

_____

_____

_____

_____

Connect the Texts
Argumentative Paragraph

Student Prompt, p. 72 Reread *Pearl and Wagner: Two Good Friends* and "Alberto, the Scientist." Who do you think are the more successful scientists, Pearl and Wagner or Alberto? Write a paragraph that states your opinion and gives evidence from the text to support it.

Writing to Sources Discuss children's opinions and the evidence they offer as support. Ask them to point out places in the texts where they found their supporting reasons. Encourage them to elaborate with additional, specific facts from the two texts to support their ideas.

	4-point Argument Writing Rubric				
Score	Statement of Purpose/Focus	Organization	Development of Evidence	Language and Vocabulary	Conventions
4	Opinion is clearly conveyed and well supported; response is focused.	Organization is clear and effective, creating a sense of cohesion.	Evidence is thorough and persuasive, and includes facts and details.	Ideas are clearly and effectively conveyed, using precise language and/or domain-specific vocabulary.	Command of conventions is strongly demonstrated.
3	Opinion is clear, adequately supported; response is generally focused.	Organization is clear, though minor flaws may be present and some ideas may be disconnected.	Evidence is adequate and includes facts and details.	Ideas are adequately conveyed, using both precise and more general language; may include domain-specific vocabulary.	Command of conventions is sufficiently demonstrated.
2	Opinion is somewhat supported; response may lack focus or include unnecessary material.	Organization is inconsistent, and flaws are apparent.	Evidence is uneven or incomplete; insufficient use of facts and details.	Ideas are unevenly conveyed, using overly-simplistic language; lack of domain-specific vocabulary.	Command of conventions is uneven.
1	The response may be confusing, unfocused; opinion not sufficiently supported.	Organization is poor or nonexistent.	Evidence is poor or nonexistent.	Ideas are conveyed in a vague, unclear, or confusing manner.	There is very little command of conventions.
0	The response shows no evidence of the ability to construct a coherent opinion essay using information from sources.				

Writing 1. Write opinion pieces in which they introduce the topic or book they are writing about, state an opinion, supply reasons that support the opinion, use linking words (e.g., because, and, also) to connect opinion and reasons, and provide a concluding statement or section.

Write Like a Reporter
Argument: Paragraph

Student Prompt Juno writes a letter without using words. Do you think words are always necessary to get a message across? Reread pages 400–402 of *Dear Juno.* Write your opinion. Support your opinion, using details from the text.

_____

_____

_____

_____

_____

_____

_____

_____

_____

_____

_____

_____

Write Like a Reporter
Argumentative Paragraph

> **Student Prompt, p. 74** Juno writes a letter without using words. Do you think words are always necessary to get a message across? Reread pages 400–402 of *Dear Juno*. Write your opinion. Support your opinion, using details from the text.

Writing to Sources Have children look for clues in the text to help them form an opinion about sending messages without words. Point out the illustrations on pages 400–401. Ask children to identify the information Juno is communicating through his drawings. Discuss children's opinions of the effectiveness of using drawings to send messages. Have them support those opinions with text evidence.

Children's paragraphs should:

- state an opinion about a topic
- supply reasons for the opinion using precise words and linking words
- use text evidence and details to support their opinion
- demonstrate strong command of the conventions of standard written English

---

© **Common Core State Standards**

Writing 1. Write opinion pieces in which they introduce the topic or book they are writing about, state an opinion, supply reasons that support the opinion, use linking words (e.g., because, and, also) to connect opinion and reasons, and provide a concluding statement or section.

Name_____

Connect the Texts

Argument: Paragraph

Student Prompt Reread *Dear Juno* and "Many Ways to Be a Soldier." In both stories, characters send a message without words. Do you think Juno and Rem chose the best ways to send their messages? Write a paragraph that states your opinion. Provide evidence from both texts to support it.

_____

_____

_____

_____

_____

_____

_____

_____

_____

_____

_____

_____

Connect the Texts

Argumentative Paragraph

> **Student Prompt, p. 76** Reread *Dear Juno* and "Many Ways to Be a Soldier."
> In both stories, characters send a message without words. Do you think Juno
> and Rem chose the best ways to send their messages? Write a paragraph that
> states your opinion. Provide evidence from both texts to support it.

Writing to Sources Discuss children's opinions. Remind them to provide
supporting evidence from both texts. Ask children to point out specific places in
the texts that offer evidence for their opinion. Have them use linking words such as
because to connect their opinion and reasons.

		4-point Argument Writing Rubric			
Score	**Statement of Purpose/Focus**	**Organization**	**Development of Evidence**	**Language and Vocabulary**	**Conventions**
4	Opinion is clearly conveyed and well supported; response is focused.	Organization is clear and effective, creating a sense of cohesion.	Evidence is thorough and persuasive, and includes facts and details.	Ideas are clearly and effectively conveyed, using precise language and/or domain-specific vocabulary.	Command of conventions is strongly demonstrated.
3	Opinion is clear, adequately supported; response is generally focused.	Organization is clear, though minor flaws may be present and some ideas may be disconnected.	Evidence is adequate and includes facts and details.	Ideas are adequately conveyed, using both precise and more general language; may include domain-specific vocabulary.	Command of conventions is sufficiently demonstrated.
2	Opinion is somewhat supported; response may lack focus or include unnecessary material.	Organization is inconsistent, and flaws are apparent.	Evidence is uneven or incomplete; insufficient use of facts and details.	Ideas are unevenly conveyed, using overly-simplistic language; lack of domain-specific vocabulary.	Command of conventions is uneven.
1	The response may be confusing, unfocused; opinion not sufficiently supported.	Organization is poor or nonexistent.	Evidence is poor or nonexistent.	Ideas are conveyed in a vague, unclear, or confusing manner.	There is very little command of conventions.
0	The response shows no evidence of the ability to construct a coherent opinion essay using information from sources.				

ⓒ Common Core State Standards

Writing 1. Write opinion pieces in which they introduce the topic or book they are writing about, state an opinion, supply reasons that support the opinion, use linking words (e.g., because, and, also) to connect opinion and reasons, and provide a concluding statement or section.

Name_____

Write Like a Reporter
Argument: Paragraph

Student Prompt Reread pages 426–427 of *Anansi Goes Fishing.* Anansi is upset after being tricked by Turtle. Do you think Anansi has a right to feel that way? Write your opinion. Supply evidence from the text to support your opinion.

_____

_____

_____

_____

_____

_____

_____

_____

_____

_____

_____

_____

_____

_____

_____

_____

_____

_____

Write Like a Reporter
Argumentative Paragraph

Student Prompt, p. 78 Reread pages 426–427 of *Anansi Goes Fishing*. Anansi is upset after being tricked by Turtle. Do you think Anansi has a right to feel that way? Write your opinion. Supply evidence from the text to support your opinion.

Writing to Sources Discuss children's opinions of Anansi's reaction to being tricked. Have children offer reasons that support their opinion. Remind them of the importance of citing evidence in the text. Ask children if their opinion was influenced by Anansi's true reason for asking for Turtle's help.

Children's paragraphs should:

- state a clear opinion about the topic
- supply reasons to support the opinion
- use evidence and facts from the text to support their reasons
- demonstrate strong command of the conventions of standard written English

---

© Common Core State Standards

Writing 1. Write opinion pieces in which they introduce the topic or book they are writing about, state an opinion, supply reasons that support the opinion, use linking words (e.g., because, and, also) to connect opinion and reasons, and provide a concluding statement or section.

Connect the Texts

Argument: Paragraph

Student Prompt Reread *Anansi Goes Fishing* and "Do spiders stick to their own webs?" Do you think Turtle could trick the spider in "Do spiders stick to their own webs?" Explain your opinion in a paragraph. Supply evidence from both texts to support your opinion.

_____

_____

_____

_____

_____

_____

_____

_____

_____

_____

_____

_____

_____

_____

Connect the Texts
Argumentative Paragraph

Student Prompt, p. 80 Reread *Anansi Goes Fishing* and "Do spiders stick to their own webs?" Do you think Turtle could trick the spider in "Do spiders stick to their own webs?" Explain your opinion in a paragraph. Supply evidence from both texts to support your opinion.

Writing to Sources Have children reread the poem on page 448 and think about the spider. Then invite them to discuss their opinion. Ask children to provide evidence from both texts to support their position. Have them provide a concluding statement in their writing that clearly states that opinion.

	4-point Argument Writing Rubric				
Score	**Statement of Purpose/Focus**	**Organization**	**Development of Evidence**	**Language and Vocabulary**	**Conventions**
4	Opinion is clearly conveyed and well supported; response is focused.	Organization is clear and effective, creating a sense of cohesion.	Evidence is thorough and persuasive, and includes facts and details.	Ideas are clearly and effectively conveyed, using precise language and/or domain-specific vocabulary.	Command of conventions is strongly demonstrated.
3	Opinion is clear, adequately supported; response is generally focused.	Organization is clear, though minor flaws may be present and some ideas may be disconnected.	Evidence is adequate and includes facts and details.	Ideas are adequately conveyed, using both precise and more general language; may include domain-specific vocabulary.	Command of conventions is sufficiently demonstrated.
2	Opinion is somewhat supported; response may lack focus or include unnecessary material.	Organization is inconsistent, and flaws are apparent.	Evidence is uneven or incomplete; insufficient use of facts and details.	Ideas are unevenly conveyed, using overly-simplistic language; lack of domain-specific vocabulary.	Command of conventions is uneven.
1	The response may be confusing, unfocused; opinion not sufficiently supported.	Organization is poor or nonexistent.	Evidence is poor or nonexistent.	Ideas are conveyed in a vague, unclear, or confusing manner.	There is very little command of conventions.
0	The response shows no evidence of the ability to construct a coherent opinion essay using information from sources.				

Ⓒ **Common Core State Standards**

Writing 1. Write opinion pieces in which they introduce the topic or book they are writing about, state an opinion, supply reasons that support the opinion, use linking words (e.g., because, and, also) to connect opinion and reasons, and provide a concluding statement or section.

Name_____

Write Like a Reporter

Argument: Paragraph

Student Prompt Reread pages 463–469 of *Rosa and Blanca.* Was it a good idea for the sisters to help each other in secret? Write your opinion and reasons for that opinion. Be sure to provide evidence from the text as support.

_____
_____
_____
_____
_____
_____
_____
_____
_____
_____
_____
_____
_____
_____
_____
_____

Write Like a Reporter

Argumentative Paragraph

> **Student Prompt, p. 82** Reread pages 463–469 of *Rosa and Blanca.* Was it a good idea for the sisters to help each other in secret? Write your opinion and reasons for that opinion. Be sure to provide evidence from the text as support.

Writing to Sources Direct children to pages 468–469. Have them think about Rosa's and Blanca's reactions as they form an opinion about the sisters' decision to help each other secretly. Discuss children's opinions of that decision. Remind them to support those opinions with specific evidence from the text.

Children's paragraphs should:

- state a clear opinion about a topic
- supply reasons for the opinion
- provide some sense of closure by drawing conclusions based on text evidence
- demonstrate strong command of the conventions of standard written English

Ⓒ **Common Core State Standards**

Writing 1. Write opinion pieces in which they introduce the topic or book they are writing about, state an opinion, supply reasons that support the opinion, use linking words (e.g., because, and, also) to connect opinion and reasons, and provide a concluding statement or section.

Name_____

Connect the Texts

Argument: Paragraph

> **Student Prompt** Reread *Rosa and Blanca* and "The Crow and the Pitcher." In the first story, the sisters often work together. In the second story, the crow solves a problem by herself. Do you think it is better to get a job done with the help of others, or by yourself? Write a paragraph. State your opinion, using evidence from each text as support.

_____

_____

_____

_____

_____

_____

_____

_____

_____

_____

_____

_____

_____

_____

Connect the Texts
Argumentative Paragraph

Student Prompt, p. 84 Reread *Rosa and Blanca* and "The Crow and the Pitcher." In the first story, the sisters often work together. In the second story, the crow solves a problem by herself. Do you think it is better to get a job done with the help of others, or by yourself? Write a paragraph. State your opinion, using evidence from each text as support.

Writing to Sources Remind children to consider evidence in both texts as they form an opinion about working with others or alone. Ask them to share their opinion, using this evidence as support. If children are having trouble forming an opinion, you may wish to prompt them to consider if the crow would have been able to reach the water faster if she had help.

	4-point Argument Writing Rubric				
Score	Statement of Purpose/Focus	Organization	Development of Evidence	Language and Vocabulary	Conventions
4	Opinion is clearly conveyed and well supported; response is focused.	Organization is clear and effective, creating a sense of cohesion.	Evidence is thorough and persuasive, and includes facts and details.	Ideas are clearly and effectively conveyed, using precise language and/or domain-specific vocabulary.	Command of conventions is strongly demonstrated.
3	Opinion is clear, adequately supported; response is generally focused.	Organization is clear, though minor flaws may be present and some ideas may be disconnected.	Evidence is adequate and includes facts and details.	Ideas are adequately conveyed, using both precise and more general language; may include domain-specific vocabulary.	Command of conventions is sufficiently demonstrated.
2	Opinion is somewhat supported; response may lack focus or include unnecessary material.	Organization is inconsistent, and flaws are apparent.	Evidence is uneven or incomplete; insufficient use of facts and details.	Ideas are unevenly conveyed, using overly-simplistic language; lack of domain-specific vocabulary.	Command of conventions is uneven.
1	The response may be confusing, unfocused; opinion not sufficiently supported.	Organization is poor or nonexistent.	Evidence is poor or nonexistent.	Ideas are conveyed in a vague, unclear, or confusing manner.	There is very little command of conventions.
0	The response shows no evidence of the ability to construct a coherent opinion essay using information from sources.				

Ⓒ Common Core State Standards

Writing 1. Write opinion pieces in which they introduce the topic or book they are writing about, state an opinion, supply reasons that support the opinion, use linking words (e.g., because, and, also) to connect opinion and reasons, and provide a concluding statement or section.

Write Like a Reporter

Argument: Paragraph

Student Prompt Reread pages 494–506 of *A Weed Is a Flower.* George Washington Carver had many talents, but he chose to study agriculture. Do you think he made a good choice? Write your opinion. Remember to support your opinion with text evidence.

_____

_____

_____

_____

_____

_____

_____

_____

_____

_____

_____

_____

_____

_____

_____

_____

_____

_____

Write Like a Reporter

Argumentative Paragraph

Student Prompt, p. 86 Reread pages 494–506 of *A Weed Is a Flower*. George Washington Carver had many talents, but he chose to study agriculture. Do you think he made a good choice? Write your opinion. Remember to support your opinion with text evidence.

Writing to Sources Discuss children's opinions of George Washington Carver's choice to study agriculture. Ask children to locate evidence in the text to support their opinion.

Pages 501–506 are especially helpful for children whose opinion is that Carver made a good choice. Have children include persuasive words in their opinion pieces such as *best* or *important*.

Children's paragraphs should:

- state an opinion about a topic
- supply reasons for the opinion using precise words and linking words
- use text evidence and details to support their opinion
- demonstrate strong command of the conventions of standard written English

© **Common Core State Standards**

Writing 1. Write opinion pieces in which they introduce the topic or book they are writing about, state an opinion, supply reasons that support the opinion, use linking words (e.g., because, and, also) to connect opinion and reasons, and provide a concluding statement or section.

Name_____

Connect the Texts

Argument: Paragraph

Student Prompt Reread *A Weed Is a Flower* and "What's Made from Corn?" In the selections, foods are used to make many things. Do you think the most interesting products are made from sweet potatoes, peanuts, or corn? Write your opinion. Include supporting evidence from each text.

_____

_____

_____

_____

_____

_____

_____

_____

_____

_____

_____

_____

Connect the Texts
Argumentative Paragraph

> **Student Prompt, p. 88** Reread *A Weed Is a Flower* and "What's Made from Corn?" In the selections, foods are used to make many things. Do you think the most interesting products are made from sweet potatoes, peanuts, or corn? Write your opinion. Include supporting evidence from each text.

Writing to Sources Make a three-column chart on the board with the headings *Sweet Potatoes, Peanuts,* and *Corn.* Invite children to refer to both texts and identify products made from each food. Record their responses. Discuss children's opinions about which food makes the most interesting products. Have them provide evidence from the texts to support their opinion.

	4-point Argument Writing Rubric				
Score	**Statement of Purpose/Focus**	**Organization**	**Development of Evidence**	**Language and Vocabulary**	**Conventions**
4	Opinion is clearly conveyed and well supported; response is focused.	Organization is clear and effective, creating a sense of cohesion.	Evidence is thorough and persuasive, and includes facts and details.	Ideas are clearly and effectively conveyed, using precise language and/or domain-specific vocabulary.	Command of conventions is strongly demonstrated.
3	Opinion is clear, adequately supported; response is generally focused.	Organization is clear, though minor flaws may be present and some ideas may be disconnected.	Evidence is adequate and includes facts and details.	Ideas are adequately conveyed, using both precise and more general language; may include domain-specific vocabulary.	Command of conventions is sufficiently demonstrated.
2	Opinion is somewhat supported; response may lack focus or include unnecessary material.	Organization is inconsistent, and flaws are apparent.	Evidence is uneven or incomplete; insufficient use of facts and details.	Ideas are unevenly conveyed, using overly-simplistic language; lack of domain-specific vocabulary.	Command of conventions is uneven.
1	The response may be confusing, unfocused; opinion not sufficiently supported.	Organization is poor or nonexistent.	Evidence is poor or nonexistent.	Ideas are conveyed in a vague, unclear, or confusing manner.	There is very little command of conventions.
0	The response shows no evidence of the ability to construct a coherent opinion essay using information from sources.				

Common Core State Standards

Writing 1. Write opinion pieces in which they introduce the topic or book they are writing about, state an opinion, supply reasons that support the opinion, use linking words (e.g., because, and, also) to connect opinion and reasons, and provide a concluding statement or section.

Prove It!
Opinion Essay

The Most Important Secret Weapon

Opinion Essay

Discuss with children times they have tried to persuade someone to agree with them. Point out how important good reasons are to persuading someone. Remind children of texts and writing tasks (such as Write Like a Reporter and Connect the Texts) in which they have encountered and practiced argument or persuasive writing.

Key Features of an Opinion Essay

- states an opinion about the topic clearly
- supports the opinion with reasons and supports the reasons with facts and details
- organizes the reasons in a logical order
- includes words to link the opinion to the reasons (*because, and, for example*)
- uses persuasive words such as *best, important,* and *should* to convince readers to agree
- provides a concluding statement that usually summarizes the writer's main point

Writing Task Overview

Each unit writing task provides children with an opportunity to write to sources. To successfully complete the task, children must analyze, synthesize, and evaluate multiple complex texts and create their own written response.

The Most Important Secret Weapon

Part 1: Children will reread the selections identified from this unit. They will then respond to questions about these sources and discuss their written responses with partners.

Part 2: Children will work individually to plan, write, and revise their own opinion essay.

Scorable Products: evidence-based short responses, opinion essay

The Most Important Secret Weapon: Writing Task – Short Response

Teacher Directions:

1. Introduce the Sources Refer children to the following texts in the Student Edition:

1. "The Crow and the Pitcher" pp. 474–477

2. *A Weed Is a Flower* pp. 486–507

Explain to children that they will need to find information in these texts to answer questions. Tell children that they will also write their own opinion essays using information from the texts.

2. Provide Directions (pp. 94–95) Answer any task-related questions children may have.

3. Facilitate Collaboration After children have completed their written responses to the evidence-based short response questions, assign partners or small groups and have them discuss their responses. If children struggle to work together productively, provide them with tips and strategies for expressing their ideas and building on others'.

© Common Core State Standards

Writing 1. Write opinion pieces in which they introduce the topic or book they are writing about, state an opinion, supply reasons that support the opinion, use linking words (e.g., because, and, also) to connect opinion and reasons, and provide a concluding statement or section.

Scoring Information

Use the following 2-point scoring rubrics to evaluate children's answers to the evidence-based short response questions.

1. What problem does the main character have in each selection? Why is each problem hard to solve?

Analysis Rubric	
2	The response: • demonstrates the ability to identify and analyze story elements across the texts • includes specific details that make reference to the texts
1	The response: • demonstrates a limited ability to identify and analyze story elements across the texts • includes some details that make reference to the texts
0	A response receives no credit if it demonstrates no ability to identify and analyze story elements across the texts or includes no relevant details from the texts.

2. How do the characters solve their problems? How are their solutions similar? How are they different?

	Synthesis Rubric
2	The response: • demonstrates the ability to synthesize information from the sources in order to describe and compare kinds of creativity • includes specific details that make reference to the texts
1	The response: • demonstrates a limited ability to synthesize information from the sources in order to describe and compare kinds of creativity • includes some details that make reference to the texts
0	A response receives no credit if it demonstrates no ability to synthesize information from the sources or includes no relevant details from the texts.

Ⓒ **Common Core State Standards**

Writing 1. Write opinion pieces in which they introduce the topic or book they are writing about, state an opinion, supply reasons that support the opinion, use linking words (e.g., because, and, also) to connect opinion and reasons, and provide a concluding statement or section.

The Most Important Secret Weapon
Writing Task – Short Response

1. What problem does the main character have in each selection? Why is each problem hard to solve?

_____

_____

_____

_____

_____

_____

_____

_____

_____

_____

_____

_____

_____

_____

_____

_____

_____

_____

Name _____

2. How do the characters solve their problems? How are their solutions similar? How are they different?

The Most Important Secret Weapon: Writing Task – Opinion Essay

Teacher Directions:

1. **Provide Directions (p. 98)** Explain to children that they will now review the sources and plan, draft, and revise their opinion essays. Children will be allowed to look back at the answers they wrote to the short response questions. Read aloud the directions for the opinion essay and answer any task-related questions they may have. Children should be given paper on which to write their opinion essays.

2. **Scoring Information** Use the scoring rubric on the next page to evaluate children's opinion essays.

3. **Opinion Essay Prompt** Write an opinion essay to persuade your classmates that creativity is the most important "secret weapon" we have to make new things and find new solutions.

   Explain why creativity is such an important "secret weapon."

   What are some examples from the texts of how the characters use creativity to solve problems?

   What are some problems you have solved using creativity?

Argument Writing Rubric					
Score	Statement of Purpose/Focus	Organization	Development of Evidence	Language and Vocabulary	Conventions
4	Opinion is clearly stated and well supported in essay.	Essay contains reasons in a logical order and a conclusion.	Essay includes sufficient evidence including facts and details.	Essay uses linking and persuasive words effectively.	Essay has correct grammar, usage, spelling, capitalization, and punctuation.
3	Opinion is clear and adequately supported in essay.	Essay's reasons are adequately organized.	Essay includes adequate evidence including facts and details.	Essay uses some linking and persuasive words.	Essay has a few errors but is understandable.
2	Opinion is somewhat supported in essay.	Essay's organization is inconsistent.	Essay's evidence is insufficient.	Essay uses few linking or persuasive words.	Essay has some errors in usage, grammar, spelling, and/or punctuation.
1	Essay lacks opinion and/or support.	Essay lacks organization.	Essay lacks evidence.	Essay's language is vague or confusing.	Essay is hard to follow because of numerous errors.
0	Opinion essay receives no credit if it does not demonstrate adequate command of argument or persuasive writing traits.				

Ⓒ **Common Core State Standards**

Writing 1. Write opinion pieces in which they introduce the topic or book they are writing about, state an opinion, supply reasons that support the opinion, use linking words (e.g., because, and, also) to connect opinion and reasons, and provide a concluding statement or section.

The Most Important Secret Weapon

Writing Task – Opinion Essay

Opinion Essay Prompt

Write an opinion essay to persuade your classmates that creativity is the most important "secret weapon" we have to make new things and find new solutions.

Explain why creativity is such an important "secret weapon."

_____

- -

_____

- -

_____

_____

- -

_____

What are some examples from the texts of how the characters use creativity to solve problems?

_____

- -

_____

- -

_____

What are some problems you have solved using creativity?

_____

- -

_____

_____

- -

The Most Important Secret Weapon: Writing Task – Opinion Essay

Teacher Directions:

1. Publish Explain to children that publishing their writing is the last step in the writing process. If time permits, have children review one another's compositions and incorporate any comments their classmates have. Discuss different ways technology can be used to publish writing.

2. Present Children will now have the option to present their opinion essays. Have children read aloud their opinion essays to the class. Use the list below to offer children tips on listening and speaking.

While Listening to a Classmate...
- Listen closely and ask yourself: "Do I agree with this reason?"
- Think about how the details and examples support the reasons.

While Speaking to Classmates...
- Have good posture and eye contact.
- Speak clearly, at an appropriate pace, and with persuasive expression.

Things to Do Together...
- Ask and answer questions about reasons.
- Build on each other's ideas.

Ⓒ **Common Core State Standards**

Writing 1. Write opinion pieces in which they introduce the topic or book they are writing about, state an opinion, supply reasons that support the opinion, use linking words (e.g., because, and, also) to connect opinion and reasons, and provide a concluding statement or section.

Unit 4 Our Changing World

Writing Focus: Informative/Explanatory

Write Like a Reporter

Explanatory Paragraph

Student Prompt Look back at pages 32–34 of
A Froggy Fable. Write two lists, the first to explain what
the frog doesn't like about his changing home, and the
second to list what the caterpillar likes about change.
Then use the two lists to write a paragraph comparing
and contrasting Frog's dislikes and caterpillar's likes.

_____

_____

_____

_____

_____

_____

_____

_____

_____

_____

_____

_____

Write Like a Reporter
Informative/Explanatory Paragraph

Student Prompt, p. 102 Look back at pages 32–34 of *A Froggy Fable.* Write two lists, the first to explain what the frog doesn't like about his changing home, and the second to list what the caterpillar likes about change. Then use the two lists to write a paragraph comparing and contrasting Frog's dislikes and caterpillar's likes.

Writing to Sources Remind children to look for the precise words that will clarify the key idea of change for both characters. The facts and reasoning can be found in both the illustrations and the text.

Children's paragraphs should:

- introduce the topic
- identify and clarify key ideas with precise words
- supply supporting facts and details from text and illustrations
- demonstrate strong command of the conventions of standard written English

Ⓒ **Common Core State Standards**

Writing 2. Write informative/explanatory texts in which they introduce a topic, use facts and definitions to develop points, and provide a concluding statement or section.

Name_____

Connect the Texts
Explanatory Summary

Student Prompt Identify the main ideas of *A Froggy Fable* and "Ben the Bullfrog." Write a paragraph that summarizes each main idea. Look for facts and details to support your conclusions in the texts.

_____

_____

_____

_____

_____

_____

_____

_____

_____

_____

_____

_____

_____

_____

_____

_____

Connect the Texts
Informative/Explanatory Summary

Student Prompt, p. 104 Identify the main ideas of *A Froggy Fable* and "Ben the Bullfrog." Write a paragraph that summarizes each main idea. Look for facts and details to support your conclusions in the texts.

Writing to Sources Remind children to read each text carefully to determine their main ideas. Have children draw conclusions and develop their points from the evidence found in each story. They should also provide a concluding statement to complete their summaries.

		Informative/Explanatory Writing Rubric			
Score	Focus	Organization	Development of Evidence	Language and Vocabulary	Conventions
4	Main idea is clearly conveyed and well supported; response is focused.	Organization is clear and effective, creating a sense of cohesion.	Evidence is relevant and thorough; includes facts and details.	Ideas are clearly and effectively conveyed, using precise language and/or domain-specific vocabulary.	Command of conventions is strongly demonstrated.
3	Main idea is clear, adequately supported; response is generally focused.	Organization is clear, though minor flaws may be present and some ideas may be disconnected.	Evidence is adequate and includes facts and details.	Ideas are adequately conveyed, using both precise and more general language; may include domain-specific vocabulary.	Command of conventions is sufficiently demonstrated.
2	Main idea is somewhat supported; lacks focus or includes unnecessary material.	Organization is inconsistent, and flaws are apparent.	Evidence is uneven or incomplete; insufficient use of facts and details.	Ideas are unevenly conveyed, using overly-simplistic language; lacks domain-specific vocabulary.	Command of conventions is uneven.
1	Response may be confusing, unfocused; main idea insufficiently supported.	Organization is poor or nonexistent.	Evidence is poor or nonexistent.	Ideas are conveyed in a vague, unclear, or confusing manner.	There is very little command of conventions.
0	The response shows no evidence of the ability to construct a coherent explanatory essay using information from sources.				

ⓒ Common Core State Standards

Writing 2. Write informative/explanatory texts in which they introduce a topic, use facts and definitions to develop points, and provide a concluding statement or section.

Write Like a Reporter
Explanatory Paragraph

Student Prompt Look back at page 69 of *Life Cycle of a Pumpkin.* How do bees help pumpkin plants? Write a paragraph that explains how bees help pumpkin plants. Use supporting details from the text.

_____

- -

_____

- -

_____

- -

_____

- -

_____

- -

_____

- -

_____

- -

_____

- -

_____

- -

_____

Write Like a Reporter
Informative/Explanatory Paragraph

> **Student Prompt, p. 106** Look back at page 69 of *Life Cycle of a Pumpkin.*
> How do bees help pumpkin plants? Write a paragraph that explains how bees
> help pumpkin plants. Use supporting details from the text.

Writing to Sources Remind children to look for the facts and details explaining why
bees are important in the process of pollination. Children should use facts to support
their explanations.

Children's paragraphs should:

- identify and introduce a topic
- supply some facts and details about the topic
- use text evidence to support explanation
- demonstrate strong command of the conventions of standard written English

ⓒ **Common Core State Standards**

Writing 2. Write informative/explanatory texts in which they introduce a topic, use facts and definitions to develop points, and provide a concluding
statement or section.

Connect the Texts

Explanatory Paragraph

Student Prompt Review *Life Cycle of a Pumpkin* and "How do seeds know which way is UP?" List the steps that a pumpkin seed makes from seed to pumpkin. Using the poem on pp. 80–81, list the steps that seeds go through when they grow. How are the lists alike? How are they different? Write a paragraph to compare and contrast the information from both texts. Use the facts and details found in the texts to support your writing.

_____

_____

_____

_____

_____

_____

_____

_____

_____

_____

_____

_____

_____

_____

_____

_____

Connect the Texts
Informative/Explanatory Paragraph

Student Prompt, p. 108 Review *Life Cycle of a Pumpkin* and "How do seeds know which way is UP?" List the steps that a pumpkin seed makes from seed to pumpkin. Using the poem on pp. 80–81, list the steps that seeds go through when they grow. How are the lists alike? How are they different? Write a paragraph to compare and contrast the information from both texts. Use the facts and details found in the texts to support your writing.

Writing to Sources Explain to children that both of these texts follow the text structure of sequence to explain the growth of a pumpkin and a seed. As they write, remind them to use precise words to clarify the details and the sequence of steps. Point out that the time line in *Life Cycle of a Pumpkin* is a good tool to help understand chronology.

		Informative/Explanatory Writing Rubric			
Score	Focus	Organization	Development of Evidence	Language and Vocabulary	Conventions
4	Main idea is clearly conveyed and well supported; response is focused.	Organization is clear and effective, creating a sense of cohesion.	Evidence is relevant and thorough; includes facts and details.	Ideas are clearly and effectively conveyed, using precise language and/or domain-specific vocabulary.	Command of conventions is strongly demonstrated.
3	Main idea is clear, adequately supported; response is generally focused.	Organization is clear, though minor flaws may be present and some ideas may be disconnected.	Evidence is adequate and includes facts and details.	Ideas are adequately conveyed, using both precise and more general language; may include domain-specific vocabulary.	Command of conventions is sufficiently demonstrated.
2	Main idea is somewhat supported; lacks focus or includes unnecessary material.	Organization is inconsistent, and flaws are apparent.	Evidence is uneven or incomplete; insufficient use of facts and details.	Ideas are unevenly conveyed, using overly-simplistic language; lacks domain-specific vocabulary.	Command of conventions is uneven.
1	Response may be confusing, unfocused; main idea insufficiently supported.	Organization is poor or nonexistent.	Evidence is poor or nonexistent.	Ideas are conveyed in a vague, unclear, or confusing manner.	There is very little command of conventions.
0	The response shows no evidence of the ability to construct a coherent explanatory essay using information from sources.				

© Common Core State Standards

Writing 2. Write informative/explanatory texts in which they introduce a topic, use facts and definitions to develop points, and provide a concluding statement or section.

Write Like a Reporter

Explanatory Paragraph

> **Student Prompt** Reread pages 96–101 of *Soil*. List the four materials found in soil. In a paragraph, write a description of each material.

_____

_____

_____

_____

_____

_____

_____

_____

_____

_____

_____

Write Like a Reporter
Informative/Explanatory Paragraph

Student Prompt, p. 110 Reread pages 96–101 of *Soil*. List the four materials found in soil. In a paragraph, write a description of each material.

Writing to Sources Help children determine the main ideas in the paragraphs on pages 96–101. This will clarify the four materials found in soil. Remind them to use the facts and descriptions found in the text.

Children's paragraphs should:

- identify and introduce the topic
- supply some facts and details about the topic
- use text evidence to support explanations
- demonstrate strong command of the conventions of standard written English

Ⓒ **Common Core State Standards**

Writing 2. Write informative/explanatory texts in which they introduce a topic, use facts and definitions to develop points, and provide a concluding statement or section.

Connect the Texts

Explanatory Paragraph

Student Prompt How do the animals from "Burrowing Animals" use soil? What qualities found in soil make it a good material to use to make a home? Write a paragraph explaining how the animals use soil and why soil is a good material for their homes. Use facts and the precise words found in *Soil* to write clear explanations.

_____

_____

_____

_____

_____

_____

_____

_____

_____

_____

_____

_____

_____

_____

Connect the Texts
Explanatory Paragraph

Student Prompt, p. 112 How do the animals from "Burrowing Animals" use soil? What qualities found in soil make it a good material to use to make a home? Write a paragraph explaining how the animals use soil and why soil is a good material for their homes. Use facts and the precise words found in *Soil* to write clear explanations.

Writing to Sources Point out to children that labels and captions identify the photographs. Remind them that a lot of information is found in captions in addition to the text. Children's paragraphs should include an explanation of why soil texture and composition would affect the construction of a burrow.

Score	Focus	Organization	Development of Evidence	Language and Vocabulary	Conventions
Informative/Explanatory Writing Rubric					
4	Main idea is clearly conveyed and well supported; response is focused.	Organization is clear and effective, creating a sense of cohesion.	Evidence is relevant and thorough; includes facts and details.	Ideas are clearly and effectively conveyed, using precise language and/or domain-specific vocabulary.	Command of conventions is strongly demonstrated.
3	Main idea is clear, adequately supported; response is generally focused.	Organization is clear, though minor flaws may be present and some ideas may be disconnected.	Evidence is adequate and includes facts and details.	Ideas are adequately conveyed, using both precise and more general language; may include domain-specific vocabulary.	Command of conventions is sufficiently demonstrated.
2	Main idea is somewhat supported; lacks focus or includes unnecessary material.	Organization is inconsistent, and flaws are apparent.	Evidence is uneven or incomplete; insufficient use of facts and details.	Ideas are unevenly conveyed, using overly-simplistic language; lacks domain-specific vocabulary.	Command of conventions is uneven.
1	Response may be confusing, unfocused; main idea insufficiently supported.	Organization is poor or nonexistent.	Evidence is poor or nonexistent.	Ideas are conveyed in a vague, unclear, or confusing manner.	There is very little command of conventions.
0	The response shows no evidence of the ability to construct a coherent explanatory essay using information from sources.				

Ⓒ **Common Core State Standards**

Writing 2. Write informative/explanatory texts in which they introduce a topic, use facts and definitions to develop points, and provide a concluding statement or section.

Write Like a Reporter
Explanatory Summary

Student Prompt Write a brief summary of the main idea of *The Night the Moon Fell*. Support your conclusion with details from the text.

_____

- -

_____

- -

_____

- -

_____

- -

_____

- -

_____

- -

_____

- -

_____

- -

_____

- -

_____

- -

_____

Write Like a Reporter
Informative/Explanatory Summary

> **Student Prompt, p. 114** Write a brief summary of the main idea of *The Night the Moon Fell*. Support your conclusion with details from the text.

Writing to Sources Explain to children that they will have to read this text carefully, as there are many details that may confuse them as they focus on the main idea. They could use the chronology of events to simplify the descriptive passages.

Children's paragraphs should:

- identify the main idea
- supply a chronological order of events
- summarize using descriptive words
- demonstrate strong command of the conventions of standard written English

Ⓒ **Common Core State Standards**

Writing 2. Write informative/explanatory texts in which they introduce a topic, use facts and definitions to develop points, and provide a concluding statement or section.

The Night the Moon Fell • Unit 4 • Week 4 **115**

Connect the Texts

Explanatory Paragraph

Student Prompt If Luna's friends, the birds and the wind, had used e-mail, they may have found her sooner. Reread pages 148–151 of "A New House." Write a paragraph that identifies and explains the steps in writing an e-mail.

_____

_____

_____

_____

_____

_____

_____

_____

_____

_____

_____

_____

_____

_____

_____

_____

_____

_____

Connect the Texts
Informative/Explanatory Paragraph

Student Prompt, p. 116 If Luna's friends, the birds and the wind, had used e-mail, they may have found her sooner. Reread pages 148–151 of "A New House." Write a paragraph that identifies and explains the steps in writing an e-mail.

Writing to Sources Remind children to read the article "A New House" slowly to understand the chronology of steps needed to write an e-mail. The labels and bold type clearly identify the precise words they can use to complete their writing.

	Informative/Explanatory Writing Rubric				
Score	Focus	Organization	Development of Evidence	Language and Vocabulary	Conventions
4	Main idea is clearly conveyed and well supported; response is focused.	Organization is clear and effective, creating a sense of cohesion.	Evidence is relevant and thorough; includes facts and details.	Ideas are clearly and effectively conveyed, using precise language and/or domain-specific vocabulary.	Command of conventions is strongly demonstrated.
3	Main idea is clear, adequately supported; response is generally focused.	Organization is clear, though minor flaws may be present and some ideas may be disconnected.	Evidence is adequate and includes facts and details.	Ideas are adequately conveyed, using both precise and more general language; may include domain-specific vocabulary.	Command of conventions is sufficiently demonstrated.
2	Main idea is somewhat supported; lacks focus or includes unnecessary material.	Organization is inconsistent, and flaws are apparent.	Evidence is uneven or incomplete; insufficient use of facts and details.	Ideas are unevenly conveyed, using overly-simplistic language; lacks domain-specific vocabulary.	Command of conventions is uneven.
1	Response may be confusing, unfocused; main idea insufficiently supported.	Organization is poor or nonexistent.	Evidence is poor or nonexistent.	Ideas are conveyed in a vague, unclear, or confusing manner.	There is very little command of conventions.
0	The response shows no evidence of the ability to construct a coherent explanatory essay using information from sources.				

© **Common Core State Standards**

Writing 2. Write informative/explanatory texts in which they introduce a topic, use facts and definitions to develop points, and provide a concluding statement or section.

Write Like a Reporter

Explanatory Paragraph

Student Prompt Reread pages 170–174. The Mountain Spirit was pleased with Jade. Write a paragraph that explains what Mountain Spirit did for Jade and the villagers and how it helped them. Support your writing with facts from the story.

_____

- -

_____

- -

_____

- -

_____

- -

_____

- -

_____

- -

_____

- -

_____

- -

_____

- -

_____

Write Like a Reporter
Informative/Explanatory Paragraph

Student Prompt, p. 118 Reread pages 170–174. The Mountain Spirit was pleased with Jade. Write a paragraph that explains what Mountain Spirit did for Jade and the villagers and how it helped them. Support your writing with facts from the story.

Writing to Sources Remind children to read the text carefully to look for details to complete their explanations.

Children's paragraphs should:

- identify and introduce a topic
- supply some facts and text evidence to support the explanation
- provide a sense of closure
- demonstrate strong command of the conventions of standard written English

Ⓒ **Common Core State Standards**

Writing 2. Write informative/explanatory texts in which they introduce a topic, use facts and definitions to develop points, and provide a concluding statement or section.

Connect the Texts

Explanatory Paragraph

Student Prompt Compare the characteristics of the Mountain Spirit from *The First Tortilla* to the description of the wind in "Wind." Use specific details from each text in your paragraph.

_____

_____

_____

_____

_____

_____

_____

_____

_____

_____

_____

_____

Connect the Texts
Informative/Explanatory Paragraph

Student Prompt, p. 120 Compare the characteristics of the Mountain Spirit from *The First Tortilla* to the description of the wind in "Wind." Use specific details from each text in your paragraph.

Writing to Sources Explain to children that comparing an expository text and a legend may be confusing until they look for the main idea in each text. Both the Mountain Spirit and wind are forces of nature. Children should use details and descriptions as evidence in their comparisons. Remind them to use *like, also, both,* and *unlike* as clue words.

	Informative/Explanatory Writing Rubric				
Score	**Focus**	**Organization**	**Development of Evidence**	**Language and Vocabulary**	**Conventions**
4	Main idea is clearly conveyed and well supported; response is focused.	Organization is clear and effective, creating a sense of cohesion.	Evidence is relevant and thorough; includes facts and details.	Ideas are clearly and effectively conveyed, using precise language and/or domain-specific vocabulary.	Command of conventions is strongly demonstrated.
3	Main idea is clear, adequately supported; response is generally focused.	Organization is clear, though minor flaws may be present and some ideas may be disconnected.	Evidence is adequate and includes facts and details.	Ideas are adequately conveyed, using both precise and more general language; may include domain-specific vocabulary.	Command of conventions is sufficiently demonstrated.
2	Main idea is somewhat supported; lacks focus or includes unnecessary material.	Organization is inconsistent, and flaws are apparent.	Evidence is uneven or incomplete; insufficient use of facts and details.	Ideas are unevenly conveyed, using overly-simplistic language; lacks domain-specific vocabulary.	Command of conventions is uneven.
1	Response may be confusing, unfocused; main idea insufficiently supported.	Organization is poor or nonexistent.	Evidence is poor or nonexistent.	Ideas are conveyed in a vague, unclear, or confusing manner.	There is very little command of conventions.
0	The response shows no evidence of the ability to construct a coherent explanatory essay using information from sources.				

Ⓒ **Common Core State Standards**

Writing 2. Write informative/explanatory texts in which they introduce a topic, use facts and definitions to develop points, and provide a concluding statement or section.

Prove It!
Explanation

Academic Vocabulary

In an explanation of a process, a writer explains how something happens while describing the steps in the process. The information is organized in paragraphs in a logical sequence and may be accompanied by helpful diagrams and illustrations.

ELL

Introduce Genre Write *explanation* on the board. Explain that this word names a kind of text that informs readers about how something happens. Point out that an explanation of a process identifies each stage in a process in order and uses facts and definitions to describe and explain the process. Discuss with children the key features of an explanation of a process that appear on this page.

A Bird Grows Up

Explanation

In this unit, children have read examples of explanatory writing, including explanations of natural processes, and have had the opportunity to write in this mode. Remind children of texts and writing tasks (such as Write like a Reporter and Connect the Texts) in which they have encountered and practiced informative/explanatory writing.

Key Features of an Explanation of a Process

- explains a process clearly using facts, details, and definitions
- groups related information, organizing it to show stages in the process
- includes formatting when useful in aiding comprehension
- addresses matters such as size, function, or behavior or how things work or why they happen
- uses words such as *first, then,* and *after that* to indicate the order of steps in the process
- provides a concluding statement or section related to the topic

Writing Task Overview

Each unit writing task provides children with an opportunity to write to sources. To successfully complete the task, children must analyze, synthesize, and evaluate multiple complex texts and create their own written response.

A Bird Grows Up

Part 1: Children will reread the selections identified from this unit. They will then respond to questions about these sources and discuss their written responses with partners.

Part 2: Children will work individually to plan, write, and revise their own explanation of a process.

Scorable Products: evidence-based short responses, explanation

A Bird Grows Up: Writing Task – Short Response

Teacher Directions:

1. Introduce the Sources Refer children to the following texts in the Student Edition:

1. *Life Cycle of a Pumpkin* pp. 62–75

2. *Soil* pp. 92–109

Explain to children that they will need to find information in these texts to answer questions. Tell children that they will also write their own explanation of a process using information from the texts.

2. Provide Directions (pp. 126–127) Answer any task-related questions children may have.

3. Facilitate Collaboration After children have completed their written responses to the evidence-based short response questions, assign partners or small groups and have them discuss their responses. If children struggle to work together productively, provide them with tips and strategies for expressing their ideas and building on others'

Ⓒ **Common Core State Standards**

Writing 2. Write informative/explanatory texts in which they introduce a topic, use facts and definitions to develop points, and provide a concluding statement or section.

Scoring Information

Use the following 2-point scoring rubrics to evaluate children's answers to the evidence-based short response questions.

1. Which explanation is easier for you to understand? Which format would you use to explain how a baby bird grows?

	Analysis Rubric
2	The response: • demonstrates the ability to analyze and compare the complexity of the processes described in the texts • includes specific details that make reference to the texts
1	The response: • demonstrates a limited ability to analyze and compare the complexity of the processes described in the texts • includes some details that make reference to the texts
0	A response receives no credit if it demonstrates no ability to analyze and compare the complexity of the processes described in the texts or includes no relevant details from the texts.

2. List the characteristics of a good explanation of a process. Tell which of the selections illustrates these characteristics best and why.

Evaluation Rubric	
2	The response: • demonstrates the ability to evaluate texts in order to create a complete list of the characteristics of a good explanation of a process • includes specific details that make reference to the texts
1	The response: • demonstrates a limited ability to evaluate texts in order to create a complete list of the characteristics of a good explanation of a process • includes some details that make reference to the texts
0	A response receives no credit if it demonstrates no ability to evaluate texts in order to create a complete list of characteristics of a good explanation of a process or includes no relevant details from the texts.

© **Common Core State Standards**

Writing 2. Write informative/explanatory texts in which they introduce a topic, use facts and definitions to develop points, and provide a concluding statement or section.

A Bird Grows Up

Writing Task – Short Response

I. Which explanation is easier for you to understand? Which format would you use to explain how a baby bird grows?

_____
_____
_____
_____
_____
_____
_____
_____
_____
_____
_____
_____
_____
_____
_____
_____
_____
_____

2. List the characteristics of a good explanation of a process. Tell which of the selections illustrates these characteristics best and why.

_____

_____

_____

_____

_____

_____

_____

_____

_____

_____

_____

A Bird Grows Up: Writing Task – Explanation

Teacher Directions:

1. **Provide Directions (p. 130)** Explain to children that they will now review the sources and plan, draft, and revise their explanations. Children will be allowed to look back at the answers they wrote to the short response questions. Read aloud the directions for the explanation of a process and answer any task-related questions they may have. Children should be given paper on which to write their explanation of a process.

2. **Scoring Information** Use the scoring rubric on the next page to evaluate children's explanations.

3. **Explanation Prompt** Write an explanation of the stages in the life of a bird, from egg to adult. Your explanation should describe the bird at each stage using time-order words and diagrams or illustrations.

Informative/Explanatory Writing Rubric					
Score	**Statement of Purpose/Focus**	**Organization**	**Development of Evidence**	**Language and Vocabulary**	**Conventions**
4	Explanation's topic is clearly stated and well supported with evidence.	Explanation's organization includes an introduction, body, and conclusion.	Explanation's evidence is thorough and carefully presented.	Explanation uses precise language to present ideas effectively.	Explanation has correct grammar, usage, spelling, capitalization, and punctuation.
3	Explanation's topic is stated and adequately supported with evidence.	Explanation's organization is clear, but some ideas are not well connected.	Explanation's evidence is adequate.	Explanation uses more general language to convey ideas adequately.	Explanation has a few errors but is understandable.
2	Explanation's topic is stated but lacks sufficient support.	Explanation's organization is inconsistent.	Explanation's evidence is incomplete or insufficient.	Explanation uses overly simple language; ideas are not clearly stated.	Explanation has some errors in usage, grammar, spelling, and/or punctuation.
1	Explanation's topic is unclear and insufficiently supported.	Explanation lacks organization.	Explanation lacks sufficient evidence.	Explanation's ideas are unclear or confusing.	Explanation is hard to follow because of numerous errors.
0	Explanation of a process receives no credit if it does not demonstrate adequate command of informative/ explanatory writing traits.				

Ⓒ Common Core State Standards

Writing 2. Write informative/explanatory texts in which they introduce a topic, use facts and definitions to develop points, and provide a concluding statement or section.

A Bird Grows Up

Writing Task – Explanation

Explanation Prompt

Write an explanation of the stages in the life of a bird, from egg to adult.

Your explanation should describe the bird at each stage using time-order words and diagrams or illustrations.

What is an egg? What is happening inside the egg?

_____

_____

_____

What comes after the egg stage?

_____

_____

_____

What is a baby bird like?

_____

_____

_____

What is an adult bird like?

_____

_____

A Bird Grows Up: Writing Task – Explanation

Teacher Directions:

1. Publish Explain to children that publishing their writing is the last step in the writing process. If time permits, have children review one another's compositions and incorporate any comments their classmates have. Discuss different ways technology can be used to publish writing.

2. Present Children will now have the option to present their explanations of a process. Have children give a "nature talk" on their explanation of a bird's life cycle in front of the class. Use the list below to offer children tips on listening and speaking.

While Listening to a Classmate...
- Face the speaker to listen attentively.
- Take notes on what the speaker says.

While Speaking to Classmates...
- Determine your purpose for speaking.
- Have good posture and eye contact.
- Speak at an appropriate pace.

Things to Do Together...
- Ask and answer questions with detail.
- Build on each other's ideas.

Ⓒ Common Core State Standards

Writing 2. Write informative/explanatory texts in which they introduce a topic, use facts and definitions to develop points, and provide a concluding statement or section.

Unit 5 Responsibility

Writing Focus: Narrative

Name_____

Write Like a Reporter
Narrative Story

Student Prompt Look back at *Fire Fighter!* What happens first? What is the problem? What is the solution? Use details from the text to write your own story about a fire. Include specific vocabulary from the selection to support your story.

_____
- -
_____
- -
_____
- -
_____
- -
_____
- -
_____
- -
_____
- -
_____
- -
_____
- -
_____

Write Like a Reporter
Narrative Story

> **Student Prompt, p. 134** Look back at *Fire Fighter!* What happens first? What is the problem? What is the solution? Use details from the text to write your own story about a fire. Include specific vocabulary from the selection to support your story.

Writing to Sources Briefly discuss with children the sequence of events in *Fire Fighter!* Then have children scan the selection for fire-related vocabulary. Make a class list of these terms and ask children to use as many as possible to support their narratives.

Children's narratives should:

- provide a setting, narrator, and characters
- include a chronology of events that reflects those in the text
- use descriptive words and sensory details from the story in the retelling of events
- demonstrate strong command of the conventions of standard written English

Ⓒ **Common Core State Standards**

Writing 3. Write narratives in which they recount a well-elaborated event or short sequence of events, include details to describe actions, thoughts, and feelings, use temporal words to signal event order, and provide a sense of closure.

Connect the Texts
Narrative Story

Student Prompt Look back at *Fire Fighter!* and "Firefighting Teamwork." Think about things the characters do in the fire stations. How are they similar? How are they like things you do at home? Write a story about life at a fire station. Use details from the two selections to support your writing.

_____

- -

_____

_____

- -

_____

_____

- -

_____

_____

- -

_____

_____

- -

_____

_____

- -

_____

_____

- -

_____

Connect the Texts
Narrative Story

Student Prompt, p. 136 Look back at *Fire Fighter!* and "Firefighting Teamwork." Think about things the characters do in the fire stations. How are they similar? How are they like things you do at home? Write a story about life at a fire station. Use details from the two selections to support your writing.

Writing to Sources Review *Fire Fighter!* and "Firefighting Teamwork" with children. Have children look through the selections and name things the characters do at a fire station that are like things people do at home. List their ideas for them. Have children use the list to support their stories.

		4-point Narrative Writing Rubric			
Score	Narrative Focus	Organization	Development of Narrative	Language and Vocabulary	Conventions
4	Narrative is clearly focused and developed throughout.	Narrative has a well-developed, logical, easy-to-follow plot.	Narrative includes thorough and effective use of details, dialogue, and description.	Narrative uses precise, concrete sensory language as well as figurative language and/or domain-specific vocabulary.	Narrative has correct grammar, usage, spelling, capitalization, and punctuation.
3	Narrative is mostly focused and developed throughout.	Narrative has a plot, but there may be some lack of clarity and/or unrelated events.	Narrative includes adequate use of details, dialogue, and description.	Narrative uses adequate sensory and figurative language and/or domain-specific vocabulary.	Narrative has a few errors but is completely understandable.
2	Narrative is somewhat developed but may occasionally lose focus.	Narrative's plot is difficult to follow, and ideas are not connected well.	Narrative includes only a few details, dialogue, and description.	Language in narrative is not precise or sensory; lacks domain-specific vocabulary.	Narrative has some errors in usage, grammar, spelling, and/or punctuation.
1	Narrative may be confusing, unfocused, or too short.	Narrative has little or no apparent plot.	Narrative includes few or no details, dialogue, or description.	Language in narrative is vague, unclear, or confusing.	Narrative is hard to follow because of frequent errors.
0	Narrative gets no credit if it does not demonstrate adequate command of narrative writing traits.				

© Common Core State Standards

Writing 3. Write narratives in which they recount a well-elaborated event or short sequence of events, include details to describe actions, thoughts, and feelings, use temporal words to signal event order, and provide a sense of closure.

Name_____

Write Like a Reporter
Narrative Story

Student Prompt Look back at pages 234–235 in *Carl the Complainer.* Think of something that you would support in your school or neighborhood. How could you help? Write a story in which you help support a good cause. Use details from *Carl the Complainer* for support.

_____

- -

_____

- -

_____

- -

_____

- -

_____

- -

_____

- -

_____

- -

_____

- -

_____

Write Like a Reporter
Narrative Story

> **Student Prompt, p. 138** Look back at pages 234–235 in *Carl the Complainer*. Think of something that you would support in your school or neighborhood. How could you help? Write a story in which you help support a good cause. Use details from *Carl the Complainer* for support.

Writing to Sources Discuss with children the events in *Carl the Complainer*. What methods did Carl and Dale use to get support? What problems did they face and what solutions did they find? Help children brainstorm writing topics and suggest they use details from the selection to aid their writing.

Children's narratives should:

- provide a setting, characters, and narrator
- include events in a sequence
- use descriptive words and details that identify events
- demonstrate strong command of the conventions of standard written English

© **Common Core State Standards**

Writing 3. Write narratives in which they recount a well-elaborated event or short sequence of events, include details to describe actions, thoughts, and feelings, use temporal words to signal event order, and provide a sense of closure.

Connect the Texts

Narrative Journal Entry

Student Prompt Look back at *Carl the Complainer* and "Fishermen." The children in *Carl the Complainer* love their park. The "sea folks" in the poem love the sea. Write a journal entry about a place that is important to you. Use descriptive language to support your writing.

_____
_____
_____
_____
_____
_____
_____
_____
_____
_____
_____
_____
_____
_____
_____
_____

Connect the Texts
Narrative Journal Entry

Student Prompt, p. 140 Look back at *Carl the Complainer* and "Fishermen." The children in *Carl the Complainer* love their park. The "sea folks" in the poem love the sea. Write a journal entry about a place that is important to you. Use descriptive language to support your writing.

Writing to Sources Review *Carl the Complainer* and "Fishermen" with children. Discuss reasons why the park and the sea are so important to the characters from each selection. List those reasons in a T-chart. Suggest children list reasons that their selected place is important to them. Remind them to focus on a place and to strengthen their writing with descriptive details.

4-point Narrative Writing Rubric					
Score	**Narrative Focus**	**Organization**	**Development of Narrative**	**Language and Vocabulary**	**Conventions**
4	Narrative is clearly focused and developed throughout.	Narrative has a well-developed, logical, easy-to-follow plot.	Narrative includes thorough and effective use of details, dialogue, and description.	Narrative uses precise, concrete sensory language as well as figurative language and/or domain-specific vocabulary.	Narrative has correct grammar, usage, spelling, capitalization, and punctuation.
3	Narrative is mostly focused and developed throughout.	Narrative has a plot, but there may be some lack of clarity and/or unrelated events.	Narrative includes adequate use of details, dialogue and description.	Narrative uses adequate sensory and figurative language and/or domain-specific vocabulary.	Narrative has a few errors but is completely understandable.
2	Narrative is somewhat developed but may occasionally lose focus.	Narrative's plot is difficult to follow, and ideas are not connected well.	Narrative includes only a few details, dialogues, and descriptions.	Language in narrative is not precise or sensory; lacks domain-specific vocabulary.	Narrative has some errors in usage, grammar, spelling and/or punctuation.
1	Narrative may be confusing, unfocused, or too short.	Narrative has little or no apparent plot.	Narrative includes few or no details, dialogue or description.	Language in narrative is vague, unclear, or confusing.	Narrative is hard to follow because of frequent errors.
0	Narrative gets no credit if it does not demonstrate adequate command of narrative writing traits.				

Ⓒ **Common Core State Standards**

Writing 3. Write narratives in which they recount a well-elaborated event or short sequence of events, include details to describe actions, thoughts, and feelings, use temporal words to signal event order, and provide a sense of closure.

Write Like a Reporter

Narrative Story

Student Prompt Look back at pages 266–270 in *Bad Dog, Dodger!* Sam discovers that taking care of a dog is a lot of work. Write a story about a pet that causes a lot of trouble. Use details from *Bad Dog, Dodger!* to support your writing.

_____

_____

_____

_____

_____

_____

_____

_____

_____

_____

_____

_____

_____

_____

_____

_____

_____

_____

Write Like a Reporter
Narrative Story

Student Prompt, p. 142 Look back at pages 266–270 in *Bad Dog, Dodger!* Sam discovers that taking care of a dog is a lot of work. Write a story about a pet that causes a lot of trouble. Use details from *Bad Dog, Dodger!* to support your writing.

Writing to Sources Discuss the sequence of events in *Bad Dog, Dodger!* with children. Help them identify that Dodger causes problems for the whole family. Help children brainstorm writing topics and suggest they use a story map to organize their thoughts. Remind children to use time-order words and descriptive details to aid their writing.

Children's narratives should:

- introduce the topic and provide a setting and characters
- include a logical sequence of events based on the text
- use details and time-order words that signify chronology in the elaboration of events
- demonstrate strong command of the conventions of standard written English

Ⓒ **Common Core State Standards**

Writing 3. Write narratives in which they recount a well-elaborated event or short sequence of events, include details to describe actions, thoughts, and feelings, use temporal words to signal event order, and provide a sense of closure.

Connect the Texts
Narrative Letter

Student Prompt Look back at *Bad Dog, Dodger!* and "How to Train Your Puppy." Write a letter to Sam telling him how you were able to train a puppy. Use the suggestions in "How to Train Your Puppy" as support.

Connect the Texts
Narrative Letter

Student Prompt, p. 144 Look back at *Bad Dog, Dodger!* and "How to Train Your Puppy." Write a letter to Sam telling him how you were able to train a puppy. Use the suggestions in "How to Train Your Puppy" as support.

Writing to Sources Review the two selections with children. Discuss how Sam's method of training Dodger in *Bad Dog, Dodger!* is different from the suggestions in "How to Train Your Puppy." Suggest children use time-order words to aid the letter's progression.

4-point Narrative Writing Rubric					
Score	**Narrative Focus**	**Organization**	**Development of Narrative**	**Language and Vocabulary**	**Conventions**
4	Narrative is clearly focused and developed throughout.	Narrative has a well-developed, logical, easy-to-follow plot.	Narrative includes thorough and effective use of details, dialogue, and description.	Narrative uses precise, concrete sensory language as well as figurative language and/or domain-specific vocabulary.	Narrative has correct grammar, usage, spelling, capitalization, and punctuation.
3	Narrative is mostly focused and developed throughout.	Narrative has a plot, but there may be some lack of clarity and/or unrelated events.	Narrative includes adequate use of details, dialogue and description.	Narrative uses adequate sensory and figurative language and/or domain-specific vocabulary.	Narrative has a few errors but is completely understandable.
2	Narrative is somewhat developed but may occasionally lose focus.	Narrative's plot is difficult to follow, and ideas are not connected well.	Narrative includes only a few details, dialogues, and descriptions.	Language in narrative is not precise or sensory; lacks domain-specific vocabulary.	Narrative has some errors in usage, grammar, spelling and/or punctuation.
1	Narrative may be confusing, unfocused, or too short.	Narrative has little or no apparent plot.	Narrative includes few or no details, dialogue or description.	Language in narrative is vague, unclear, or confusing.	Narrative is hard to follow because of frequent errors.
0	Narrative gets no credit if it does not demonstrate adequate command of narrative writing traits.				

© Common Core State Standards

Writing 3. Write narratives in which they recount a well-elaborated event or short sequence of events, include details to describe actions, thoughts, and feelings, use temporal words to signal event order, and provide a sense of closure.

Write Like a Reporter
Narrative Story

Student Prompt Look back at pages 298–301 in *Horace and Morris but mostly Dolores.* The three friends do many different things together. What do you like to do with your friends? Write a story about something you did with your friends. Use descriptive words to make your story better.

_____
- -
_____
- -
_____
- -
_____
- -
_____
- -
_____
- -
_____
- -
_____
- -
_____
- -
_____
- -
_____

Write Like a Reporter
Narrative Story

Student Prompt, p. 146 Look back at pages 298–301 in *Horace and Morris but mostly Dolores.* The three friends do many different things together. What do you like to do with your friends? Write a story about something you did with your friends. Use descriptive words to make your story better.

Writing to Sources Look back at the story and illustrations with children. Have them use the illustrations to identify things the friends do together. Then have them think of a favorite memory or activity they did with their friends. Remind children to use time-order words and descriptive details to support their writing.

Children's narratives should:

- provide a setting, narrator, and characters
- recount events in a clear sequence
- use time-order and descriptive words and details that identify events
- demonstrate strong command of the conventions of standard written English

Ⓒ **Common Core State Standards**

Writing 3. Write narratives in which they recount a well-elaborated event or short sequence of events, include details to describe actions, thoughts, and feelings, use temporal words to signal event order, and provide a sense of closure.

Connect the Texts
Narrative Story

Student Prompt Look back at *Horace and Morris but mostly Dolores* and "Good Kicking." These selections tell us that boys and girls can have fun playing together. Choose a sport you would like to play. Write a story about how the girls and boys on your team won a big game. Use descriptive words to support your writing.

_____

_____

_____

_____

_____

_____

_____

_____

_____

_____

_____

_____

_____

_____

_____

_____

Connect the Texts
Narrative Story

Student Prompt, p. 148 Look back at *Horace and Morris but mostly Dolores* and "Good Kicking." These selections tell us that boys and girls can have fun playing together. Choose a sport you would like to play. Write a story about how the girls and boys on your team won a big game. Use descriptive words to support your writing.

Writing to Sources Review the two selections with children. How do the characters feel when boys and girls are separated? How do they feel when they play together? Compile a list of team sports for children to choose from. Remind them to use time-order and descriptive words.

		4-point Narrative Writing Rubric			
Score	**Narrative Focus**	**Organization**	**Development of Narrative**	**Language and Vocabulary**	**Conventions**
4	Narrative is clearly focused and developed throughout.	Narrative has a well-developed, logical, easy-to-follow plot.	Narrative includes thorough and effective use of details, dialogue, and description.	Narrative uses precise, concrete sensory language as well as figurative language and/or domain-specific vocabulary.	Narrative has correct grammar, usage, spelling, capitalization, and punctuation.
3	Narrative is mostly focused and developed throughout.	Narrative has a plot, but there may be some lack of clarity and/or unrelated events.	Narrative includes adequate use of details, dialogue and description.	Narrative uses adequate sensory and figurative language and/or domain-specific vocabulary.	Narrative has a few errors but is completely understandable.
2	Narrative is somewhat developed but may occasionally lose focus.	Narrative's plot is difficult to follow, and ideas are not connected well.	Narrative includes only a few details, dialogues, and descriptions.	Language in narrative is not precise or sensory; lacks domain-specific vocabulary.	Narrative has some errors in usage, grammar, spelling and/or punctuation.
1	Narrative may be confusing, unfocused, or too short.	Narrative has little or no apparent plot.	Narrative includes few or no details, dialogue or description.	Language in narrative is vague, unclear, or confusing.	Narrative is hard to follow because of frequent errors.
0	Narrative gets no credit if it does not demonstrate adequate command of narrative writing traits.				

© **Common Core State Standards**

Writing 3. Write narratives in which they recount a well-elaborated event or short sequence of events, include details to describe actions, thoughts, and feelings, use temporal words to signal event order, and provide a sense of closure.

Write Like a Reporter

Narrative Story

Student Prompt Reread pages 337–345 in *The Signmaker's Assistant.* Norman's signs cause trouble for the whole town. Write a story about another problem that Norman's signs cause. Use details and illustrations from the text to write your story.

_____

_____

_____

_____

_____

_____

_____

_____

_____

_____

_____

_____

_____

_____

_____

_____

_____

_____

Write Like a Reporter
Narrative Story

Student Prompt, p. 150 Reread pages 337–345 in *The Signmaker's Assistant*. Norman's signs cause trouble for the whole town. Write a story about another problem that Norman's signs cause. Use details and illustrations from the text to write your story.

Writing to Sources Look back at *The Signmaker's Assistant.* Discuss with children the different problems caused by Norman's signs. As children prepare to write, suggest they think of some other problems that signs could cause. Remind them to use evidence from the text and descriptive words to support their writing.

Children's narratives should:

- provide a setting, narrator, and characters
- include a chronology of events that reflects those in the text
- use descriptive words and sensory details from the text
- demonstrate strong command of the conventions of standard written English

Ⓒ **Common Core State Standards**

Writing 3. Write narratives in which they recount a well-elaborated event or short sequence of events, include details to describe actions, thoughts, and feelings, use temporal words to signal event order, and provide a sense of closure.

Name_____

Connect the Texts

Narrative Paragraph

Student Prompt Look back at *The Signmaker's Assistant* and "Helping Hand." Think about how these selections teach us to be responsible. Use details from the selections to write a paragraph about a time when you were responsible. Did you help someone? What was the result?

_____

_____

_____

_____

_____

_____

_____

_____

_____

_____

_____

_____

Connect the Texts
Narrative Paragraph

> **Student Prompt, p. 152** Look back at *The Signmaker's Assistant* and "Helping Hand." Think about how these selections teach us to be responsible. Use details from the selections to write a paragraph about a time when you were responsible. Did you help someone? What was the result?

Writing to Sources Review the selections with children. Discuss with them why it is important to be responsible for our actions and for the people and places around us. Allow children to share their ideas for writing. Encourage them to use descriptive language and to focus on the main idea.

4-point Narrative Writing Rubric				
Score	Narrative Focus	Organization	Development of Narrative	Language and Vocabulary	Conventions
4	Narrative is clearly focused and developed throughout.	Narrative has a well-developed, logical, easy-to-follow plot.	Narrative includes thorough and effective use of details, dialogue, and description.	Narrative uses precise, concrete sensory language as well as figurative language and/or domain-specific vocabulary.	Narrative has correct grammar, usage, spelling, capitalization, and punctuation.
3	Narrative is mostly focused and developed throughout.	Narrative has a plot, but there may be some lack of clarity and/or unrelated events.	Narrative includes adequate use of details, dialogue and description.	Narrative uses adequate sensory and figurative language and/or domain-specific vocabulary.	Narrative has a few errors but is completely understandable.
2	Narrative is somewhat developed but may occasionally lose focus.	Narrative's plot is difficult to follow, and ideas are not connected well.	Narrative includes only a few details, dialogues, and descriptions.	Language in narrative is not precise or sensory; lacks domain-specific vocabulary.	Narrative has some errors in usage, grammar, spelling and/or punctuation.
1	Narrative may be confusing, unfocused, or too short.	Narrative has little or no apparent plot.	Narrative includes few or no details, dialogue or description.	Language in narrative is vague, unclear, or confusing.	Narrative is hard to follow because of frequent errors.
0	Narrative gets no credit if it does not demonstrate adequate command of narrative writing traits.				

Ⓒ Common Core State Standards

Writing 3. Write narratives in which they recount a well-elaborated event or short sequence of events, include details to describe actions, thoughts, and feelings, use temporal words to signal event order, and provide a sense of closure.

Prove It!
Story

Academic Vocabulary

A story is about characters and what they do. It has a setting and a plot. It can be about something real or something imaginary.

ELL

Introduce Genre Write *story* on the board. Explain that this word names a particular kind of writing. The people or animals in a story are the characters. The time and place of the story are the setting. The events in the story are the plot. Discuss with children the key features of a story that appear on this page.

Problem Solvers

Story

In this unit, children have read examples of narrative writing, including several stories, and have had the opportunity to write in this mode. Remind children of texts and writing tasks (such as Write Like a Reporter and Connect the Texts) in which they have encountered and practiced narrative writing.

Key Features of a Story

- has characters, a setting, and a plot
- involves characters in solving a problem
- includes description and dialogue to report what a place is like and what characters say and do
- has a beginning, middle, and end
- uses punctuation and emphasis, such as quotation marks for characters' words and exclamation marks and all capital letters to show emotion

Writing Task Overview

Each unit writing task provides children with an opportunity to write to sources. To successfully complete the task, children must analyze, synthesize, and evaluate multiple complex texts and create their own extended written response.

Problem Solvers

Part 1: Children will reread the selections identified from this unit. They will then respond to questions about these sources and discuss their written responses.

Part 2: Children will work individually to plan, write, and revise their own story.

Scorable Products: evidence-based short responses, story

Problem Solvers: Writing Task – Short Response

Teacher Directions:

1. Introduce the Sources Refer children to the following texts in the Student Edition:

1. *Carl the Complainer* pp. 230–247

2. *Bad Dog, Dodger!* pp. 264–277

Explain to children that they will need to find information in these texts to answer questions. Tell children that they will also write their own stories using information from the texts.

2. Provide Directions (pp. 158–159) Answer any task-related questions children may have.

3. Facilitate Collaboration After children have completed their written responses to the evidence-based short response questions, assign partners or small groups and have them discuss their responses. If children struggle to work together productively, provide them with tips and strategies for expressing their ideas and building on others'.

Ⓒ **Common Core State Standards**

Writing 3. Write narratives in which they recount a well-elaborated event or short sequence of events, include details to describe actions, thoughts, and feelings, use temporal words to signal event order, and provide a sense of closure.

Scoring Information

Use the following 2-point scoring rubrics to evaluate children's answers to the evidence-based short response questions.

1. What problems must be solved in both stories? How do the characters solve the problems? What skills do the characters have?

	Analysis Rubric	
2	The response: • demonstrates the ability to identify and analyze character, plot, and theme elements among the texts • includes specific details that make reference to the texts	
1	The response: • demonstrates a limited ability to identify and analyze character, plot, and theme elements among the texts • includes some details that make reference to the texts	
0	A response receives no credit if it demonstrates no ability to identify and analyze character, plot, and theme elements among the texts or includes no relevant details from the texts.	

2. Think about what it means to be responsible. Do you think that these characters are responsible? Explain why or why not.

	Evaluation Rubric	
2	The response: • demonstrates the ability to evaluate texts in order to define an abstract quality and exemplify it using text examples • includes specific details that make reference to the texts	
1	The response: • demonstrates a limited ability to evaluate texts in order to define an abstract quality and exemplify it using text examples • includes some details that make reference to the texts	
0	A response receives no credit if it demonstrates no ability to evaluate texts in order to define an abstract quality and exemplify it using text examples.	

ⓒ Common Core State Standards

Writing 3. Write narratives in which they recount a well-elaborated event or short sequence of events, include details to describe actions, thoughts, and feelings, use temporal words to signal event order, and provide a sense of closure.

Name _____

Problem Solvers

Writing Task – Short Response

I. What problems must be solved in both stories?
How do the characters solve the problems?
What skills do the characters have?

_____

_____

_____

_____

_____

_____

_____

_____

_____

_____

_____

_____

Name _____

2. Think about what it means to be responsible.
Do you think that these characters are
responsible? Explain why or why not.

_____

- -

_____

- -

_____

- -

_____

- -

_____

- -

_____

- -

_____

- -

_____

- -

_____

- -

_____

Problem Solvers: Writing Task – Story

Teacher Directions:

1. **Provide Directions (p. 162)** Explain to children that they will now review the sources and plan, draft, and revise their stories. Children will be allowed to look back at the answers they wrote to the short response questions. Read aloud the directions for the story and answer any task-related questions they may have. Children should be given paper on which to write their story.

2. **Scoring Information** Use the scoring rubric on the next page to evaluate children's stories.

3. **Story Prompt** Write a story in which the characters from the different selections find a way to solve the problem of a dirty park by making visitors act responsibly. Your story should include what you want to do, how you do it, and how you feel about helping.

Narrative Writing Rubric

Score	Statement of Purpose	Organization	Development of Narrative	Language and Vocabulary	Conventions
4	Story is carefully developed.	Story has a well-developed, easy-to-follow plot.	Story includes effective use of description and dialogue.	Story uses sensory language effectively.	Story has correct grammar, usage, spelling, capitalization, and punctuation.
3	Story is mostly developed.	Story has a plot with some unrelated events.	Story includes adequate use of description and dialogue.	Story uses some sensory language.	Story has a few errors but is understandable.
2	Story is somewhat developed.	Story's plot is confusing.	Story includes only a little description and dialogue.	Story's language is not sensory.	Story has some errors in usage, grammar, spelling, and/or punctuation.
1	Story is confusing.	Story has little or no plot.	Story includes no description or dialogue.	Story's language is vague or confusing.	Story is hard to follow because of numerous errors.
0	Story receives no credit if it does not demonstrate adequate command of narrative writing traits.				

Common Core State Standards

Writing 3. Write narratives in which they recount a well-elaborated event or short sequence of events, include details to describe actions, thoughts, and feelings, use temporal words to signal event order, and provide a sense of closure.

Name _____

Problem Solvers

Writing Task – Story

Story Prompt

Write a story in which the characters from the different selections find a way to solve the problem of a dirty park by making visitors act responsibly. Your story should include what you want to do, how you do it, and how you feel about helping.

What do you want to do when you see the problem?

_____

- -

_____

- -

_____

How do you fix the problem?

_____

- -

_____

- -

_____

- -

_____

How do you feel about helping to fix the problem?

_____

- -

_____

- -

_____

Problem Solvers: Writing Task – Story

Teacher Directions:

1. Publish Explain to children that publishing their writing is the last step in the writing process. If time permits, have children review one another's compositions and incorporate any comments their classmates have. Discuss different ways technology can be used to publish writing.

2. Present Children will now have the option to present their stories. Have children give speeches on their stories in front of the class. Use the list below to offer children tips on listening and speaking.

While Listening to a Classmate...
- Face the speaker to listen attentively.
- Take notes on what the speaker says.

While Speaking to Classmates...
- Determine your purpose for speaking.
- Have good posture and eye contact.
- Speak at an appropriate pace.

Things to Do Together...
- Ask and answer questions with detail.
- Build on each other's ideas.

Ⓒ **Common Core State Standards**

Writing 3. Write narratives in which they recount a well-elaborated event or short sequence of events, include details to describe actions, thoughts, and feelings, use temporal words to signal event order, and provide a sense of closure.

Unit 6 Traditions

Writing Focus: Argument

Write Like a Reporter

Argument: Paragraph

> **Student Prompt** Review the story *Just Like Josh Gibson.* Do you think it was fair that Grandmama was not allowed to play baseball with the boys? In a paragraph, write your opinion. Provide reasons to support your opinion using evidence in the text.

_____

- -

_____

- -

_____

- -

_____

- -

_____

- -

_____

- -

_____

- -

_____

- -

_____

- -

_____

- -

_____

Write Like a Reporter
Argumentative Paragraph

Student Prompt, p. 166 Review the story *Just Like Josh Gibson.* Do you think it was fair that Grandmama was not allowed to play baseball with the boys? In a paragraph, write your opinion. Provide reasons to support your opinion using evidence in the text.

Writing to Sources Have children look for clues in *Just Like Josh Gibson* to help them form an opinion about Grandmama not being allowed to play baseball with the boys. Before children begin to write their opinion, remind them to introduce the topic, state their opinion, and then provide reasons to support their opinion. Tell them to look for evidence in the story. Encourage them to use words such as *because, and,* and *also* to connect their reasons and opinions.

Children's paragraphs should:

- introduce the topic and state an opinion
- supply reasons for the opinion using text evidence and personal experience
- use words such as *because, and,* and *also* to connect reasons and opinion
- demonstrate strong command of the conventions of standard written English

Ⓒ **Common Core State Standards**

Writing 1. Write opinion pieces in which they introduce the topic or book they are writing about, state an opinion, supply reasons that support the opinion, use linking words (e.g., because, and, also) to connect opinion and reasons, and provide a concluding statement or section.

Name_____

Connect the Texts

Argument: Paragraph

Student Prompt Reread *Just Like Josh Gibson* and "How Baseball Began." Do you think Grandmama would have been allowed to play "rounders" rather than the game "baseball" as we play it today? Use details from the selections to support your opinion.

_____

_____

_____

_____

_____

_____

_____

_____

_____

_____

_____

_____

_____

_____

_____

_____

_____

_____

_____

Connect the Texts
Argumentative Paragraph

Student Prompt, p. 168 Reread *Just Like Josh Gibson* and "How Baseball Began." Do you think Grandmama would have been allowed to play "rounders" rather than the game "baseball" as we play it today? Use details from the selections to support your opinion.

Writing to Sources Have children review the selections *Just Like Josh Gibson* and "How Baseball Began." Remind them to use details from the selections to support their opinion. Discuss the use of persuasive phrases such as *I feel, I believe,* or *in my opinion* to begin their paragraph.

		4-point Argument Writing Rubric			
Score	**Statement of Purpose/Focus**	**Organization**	**Development of Evidence**	**Language and Vocabulary**	**Conventions**
4	Opinion is clearly conveyed and well supported; response is focused.	Organization is clear and effective, creating a sense of cohesion.	Evidence is thorough and persuasive, and includes facts and details.	Ideas are clearly and effectively conveyed, using precise language and/or domain-specific vocabulary.	Command of conventions is strongly demonstrated.
3	Opinion is clear, adequately supported; response is generally focused.	Organization is clear, though minor flaws may be present and some ideas may be disconnected.	Evidence is adequate and includes facts and details.	Ideas are adequately conveyed, using both precise and more general language; may include domain-specific vocabulary.	Command of conventions is sufficiently demonstrated.
2	Opinion is somewhat supported; response may lack focus or include unnecessary material.	Organization is inconsistent, and flaws are apparent.	Evidence is uneven or incomplete; insufficient use of facts and details.	Ideas are unevenly conveyed, using overly-simplistic language; lack of domain-specific vocabulary.	Command of conventions is uneven.
1	The response may be confusing, unfocused; opinion not sufficiently supported.	Organization is poor or nonexistent.	Evidence is poor or nonexistent.	Ideas are conveyed in a vague, unclear, or confusing manner.	There is very little command of conventions.
0	The response shows no evidence of the ability to construct a coherent opinion essay using information from sources.				

©️ **Common Core State Standards**

Writing 1. Write opinion pieces in which they introduce the topic or book they are writing about, state an opinion, supply reasons that support the opinion, use linking words (e.g., *because, and, also*) to connect opinion and reasons, and provide a concluding statement or section.

Name_____

Write Like a Reporter

Argument: Paragraph

Student Prompt Review the story *Red, White, and Blue.* Is it a good idea to have one flag for an entire country? Write your opinion and include reasons that support your opinion. Use facts from the text to support your reasons.

_____

_____

_____

_____

_____

_____

_____

_____

_____

_____

_____

_____

_____

Write Like a Reporter
Argumentative Paragraph

> **Student Prompt, p. 170** Review the story *Red, White, and Blue.* Is it a good idea to have one flag for an entire country? Write your opinion and include reasons that support your opinion. Use facts from the text to support your reasons.

Writing to Sources Review the story *Red, White, and Blue* with children. Ask them if it is a good idea to have one flag represent an entire country. Remind children that their writing is going to try to persuade the reader to believe as they do. Tell them to use thinking and feeling words such as *I believe, it is my opinion, I think, I feel,* and *I hope.* Encourage them to write with certainty, using words such as *must, will, might, almost, never, have to, certain,* and *should.*

Children's paragraphs should:

- state a clear opinion about the topic
- supply reasons for the opinion using facts and details from the text
- use linking words and phrases to connect reasons with opinion
- demonstrate strong command of the conventions of standard written English

© **Common Core State Standards**

Writing 1. Write opinion pieces in which they introduce the topic or book they are writing about, state an opinion, supply reasons that support the opinion, use linking words (e.g., *because, and, also*) to connect opinion and reasons, and provide a concluding statement or section.

Connect the Texts

Argument: Paragraph

Student Prompt Reread "You're a Grand Old Flag" on pages 422–423. Make a list of the persuasive and descriptive phrases used in the song. Can these phrases be used to support different parts of the selection *Red, White, and Blue?* Write a brief paragraph stating your opinion with support from the text. Use words such as *because, first,* and *also* to connect your reasons to your opinion.

_____

_____

_____

_____

_____

_____

_____

_____

_____

_____

_____

_____

Connect the Texts

Argumentative Paragraph

Student Prompt, p. 172 Reread "You're a Grand Old Flag" on pages 422–423. Make a list of the persuasive and descriptive phrases used in the song. Can these phrases be used to support different parts of the selection *Red, White, and Blue?* Write a brief paragraph stating your opinion with support from the text. Use words such as *because, first,* and *also* to connect your reasons to your opinion.

Writing to Sources Have children reread "You're a Grand Old Flag" and look for persuasive and descriptive phrases in the song. Ask them if these same phrases support information about the U.S. Flag in *Red, White,* and *Blue.* Have children write their opinion with evidence from the text in a brief paragraph. Remind them to use linking words (e.g., *because, first, and, second, also, third, another reason*) to link their opinion with their reasons.

Score	Statement of Purpose/Focus	Organization	Development of Evidence	Language and Vocabulary	Conventions
4-point Argument Writing Rubric					
4	Opinion is clearly conveyed and well supported; response is focused.	Organization is clear and effective, creating a sense of cohesion.	Evidence is thorough and persuasive, and includes facts and details.	Ideas are clearly and effectively conveyed, using precise language and/or domain-specific vocabulary.	Command of conventions is strongly demonstrated.
3	Opinion is clear, adequately supported; response is generally focused.	Organization is clear, though minor flaws may be present and some ideas may be disconnected.	Evidence is adequate and includes facts and details.	Ideas are adequately conveyed, using both precise and more general language; may include domain-specific vocabulary.	Command of conventions is sufficiently demonstrated.
2	Opinion is somewhat supported; response may lack focus or include unnecessary material.	Organization is inconsistent, and flaws are apparent.	Evidence is uneven or incomplete; insufficient use of facts and details.	Ideas are unevenly conveyed, using overly-simplistic language; lack of domain-specific vocabulary.	Command of conventions is uneven.
1	The response may be confusing, unfocused; opinion not sufficiently supported.	Organization is poor or nonexistent.	Evidence is poor or nonexistent.	Ideas are conveyed in a vague, unclear, or confusing manner.	There is very little command of conventions.
0	The response shows no evidence of the ability to construct a coherent opinion essay using information from sources.				

© Common Core State Standards

Writing 1. Write opinion pieces in which they introduce the topic or book they are writing about, state an opinion, supply reasons that support the opinion, use linking words (e.g., *because, and, also*) to connect opinion and reasons, and provide a concluding statement or section.

Name _____

Write Like a Reporter
Argument: Paragraph

Student Prompt Reread pages 439–441 of
A Birthday Basket for Tía. Write an opinion on whether
or not Cecilia made a wonderful present. Use details
and reasons from the story to support your opinion.

_____
_____
_____
_____
_____
_____
_____
_____
_____
_____
_____
_____
_____
_____
_____
_____
_____
_____
_____

Write Like a Reporter
Argumentative Paragraph

> **Student Prompt, p. 174** Reread pages 439–441 of *A Birthday Basket for Tía*. Write an opinion on whether or not Cecilia made a wonderful present. Use details and reasons from the story to support your opinion.

Writing to Sources After children review the pages in *A Birthday Basket for Tía*, ask if they think Cecilia made a wonderful present for Tía. Have them support their opinion with reasons and details from the story. Remind children to use linking words such as *first, because,* and *also* to connect their reasons to their opinion.

Children's paragraphs should:

- state an opinion about a topic
- supply reasons for the opinion using descriptive words, facts, and details
- use words that link reasons to opinions
- demonstrate strong command of the conventions of standard written English

© **Common Core State Standards**

Writing 1. Write opinion pieces in which they introduce the topic or book they are writing about, state an opinion, supply reasons that support the opinion, use linking words (e.g., *because, and, also*) to connect opinion and reasons, and provide a concluding statement or section.

Connect the Texts

Argument: Paragraph

Student Prompt Review *A Birthday Basket for Tía* and "Family Traditions: Birthdays." Why are birthdays celebrated in different countries and in different ways? Write a brief paragraph stating your opinion and giving reasons that support your opinion. Use facts, descriptive words, and details from the texts to help persuade your readers.

Connect the Texts
Argumentative Paragraph

Student Prompt, p. 176 Review *A Birthday Basket for Tía* and "Family Traditions: Birthdays." Why are birthdays celebrated in different countries and in different ways? Write a brief paragraph stating your opinion and giving reasons that support your opinion. Use facts, descriptive words, and details from the texts to help persuade your readers.

Writing to Sources Have children review *A Birthday Basket for Tía* and "Family Traditions: Birthdays." Explain that when we write an opinion, we need to write in a way that persuades others to agree with our opinion or to think that it is the best opinion. Have children discuss how the family in *A Birthday Basket for Tía* and the different countries in "Family Traditions: Birthdays" celebrate birthdays. Then have them write a brief paragraph giving their opinion about why birthdays are celebrated, and why the traditions in various countries are different. Remind them to include reasons that support their opinion using facts, descriptive words, and details from the texts.

	4-point Argument Writing Rubric				
Score	**Statement of Purpose/Focus**	**Organization**	**Development of Evidence**	**Language and Vocabulary**	**Conventions**
4	Opinion is clearly conveyed and well supported; response is focused.	Organization is clear and effective, creating a sense of cohesion.	Evidence is thorough and persuasive, and includes facts and details.	Ideas are clearly and effectively conveyed, using precise language and/or domain-specific vocabulary.	Command of conventions is strongly demonstrated.
3	Opinion is clear, adequately supported; response is generally focused.	Organization is clear, though minor flaws may be present and some ideas may be disconnected.	Evidence is adequate and includes facts and details.	Ideas are adequately conveyed, using both precise and more general language; may include domain-specific vocabulary.	Command of conventions is sufficiently demonstrated.
2	Opinion is somewhat supported; response may lack focus or include unnecessary material.	Organization is inconsistent, and flaws are apparent.	Evidence is uneven or incomplete; insufficient use of facts and details.	Ideas are unevenly conveyed, using overly-simplistic language; lack of domain-specific vocabulary.	Command of conventions is uneven.
1	The response may be confusing, unfocused; opinion not sufficiently supported.	Organization is poor or nonexistent.	Evidence is poor or nonexistent.	Ideas are conveyed in a vague, unclear, or confusing manner.	There is very little command of conventions.
0	The response shows no evidence of the ability to construct a coherent opinion essay using information from sources.				

Ⓒ **Common Core State Standards**

Writing 1. Write opinion pieces in which they introduce the topic or book they are writing about, state an opinion, supply reasons that support the opinion, use linking words (e.g., *because, and, also*) to connect opinion and reasons, and provide a concluding statement or section.

Name_____

Write Like a Reporter

Argument: Paragraph

Student Prompt Reread pages 478–483 of *Cowboys.* Is the life of a cowboy easy or hard? Write an opinion about whether a cowboy's life is easy or hard and explain your opinion. Support your opinion with facts, details, and reasons from the text.

_____
_____
_____
_____
_____
_____
_____
_____
_____
_____
_____
_____
_____
_____
_____
_____

Write Like a Reporter
Argumentative Paragraph

> **Student Prompt, p. 178** Reread pages 478–483 of *Cowboys.* Is the life of a cowboy easy or hard? Write an opinion about whether a cowboy's life is easy or hard and explain your opinion. Support your opinion with facts, details, and reasons from the text.

Writing to Sources Have children reread the pages in *Cowboys.* Tell them they are going to write an opinion stating whether a cowboy's life is easy or hard. Remind children to use persuasive words such as *I think, I believe,* and *in my opinion,* and to use linking words such as *first, because, second, third,* and *also* to connect their reasons to their opinion. Have them use evidence from the text to support their reasons.

Children's paragraphs should:

- state a clear opinion about the topic
- supply reasons for the opinion using facts and details from the text
- use words that link reasons to an opinion
- demonstrate strong command of the conventions of standard written English

---

© **Common Core State Standards**

Writing 1. Write opinion pieces in which they introduce the topic or book they are writing about, state an opinion, supply reasons that support the opinion, use linking words (e.g., because, and, also) to connect opinion and reasons, and provide a concluding statement or section.

Connect the Texts

Argument: Paragraph

Student Prompt Reread *Cowboys* and "Cowboy Gear." Which article of clothing is the most important for the work that cowboys do? Write a brief paragraph stating your opinion. Use details found in *Cowboys* and "Cowboy Gear" to support your opinion.

_____

- -

_____

- -

_____

- -

_____

- -

_____

- -

_____

- -

_____

- -

_____

- -

_____

Connect the Texts
Argumentative Paragraph

Student Prompt, p. 180 Reread *Cowboys* and "Cowboy Gear." Which article of clothing is the most important for the work that cowboys do? Write a brief paragraph stating your opinion. Use details found in *Cowboys* and "Cowboy Gear" to support your opinion.

Writing to Sources Have children reread the selections. Discuss with children the articles of clothing that cowboys wear, and how it helps them do their work. Have children use this discussion to form an opinion. Tell children to introduce their opinion and then give reasons that support it. As they review both texts, have them write lists to refer to before writing the reasons that support their opinions.

\multicolumn{6}{c}{**4-point Argument Writing Rubric**}					
Score	**Statement of Purpose/Focus**	**Organization**	**Development of Evidence**	**Language and Vocabulary**	**Conventions**
4	Opinion is clearly conveyed and well supported; response is focused.	Organization is clear and effective, creating a sense of cohesion.	Evidence is thorough and persuasive, and includes facts and details.	Ideas are clearly and effectively conveyed, using precise language and/or domain-specific vocabulary.	Command of conventions is strongly demonstrated.
3	Opinion is clear, adequately supported; response is generally focused.	Organization is clear, though minor flaws may be present and some ideas may be disconnected.	Evidence is adequate and includes facts and details.	Ideas are adequately conveyed, using both precise and more general language; may include domain-specific vocabulary.	Command of conventions is sufficiently demonstrated.
2	Opinion is somewhat supported; response may lack focus or include unnecessary material.	Organization is inconsistent, and flaws are apparent.	Evidence is uneven or incomplete; insufficient use of facts and details.	Ideas are unevenly conveyed, using overly-simplistic language; lack of domain-specific vocabulary.	Command of conventions is uneven.
1	The response may be confusing, unfocused; opinion not sufficiently supported.	Organization is poor or nonexistent.	Evidence is poor or nonexistent.	Ideas are conveyed in a vague, unclear, or confusing manner.	There is very little command of conventions.
0	The response shows no evidence of the ability to construct a coherent opinion essay using information from sources.				

Ⓒ Common Core State Standards

Writing 1. Write opinion pieces in which they introduce the topic or book they are writing about, state an opinion, supply reasons that support the opinion, use linking words (e.g., because, and, also) to connect opinion and reasons, and provide a concluding statement or section.

Write Like a Reporter

Argument: Paragraph

Student Prompt Review the selection *Grace for President.* Did Grace or Thomas work harder to win the election? Use examples from the text to draw your conclusion and to support your opinion.

_____

_____

_____

_____

_____

_____

_____

_____

_____

_____

_____

_____

_____

_____

_____

_____

Write Like a Reporter

Argumentative Paragraph

Student Prompt, p. 182 Review the selection *Grace for President.* Did Grace or Thomas work harder to win the election? Use examples from the text to draw your conclusion and to support your opinion.

Writing to Sources Have children review *Grace for President.* Ask them who worked harder to win the election, Grace or Thomas. Remind children to make their opinion clear by using persuasive words such as *I think, I believe,* and *in my opinion,* and to use linking words such as *first, because,* and *also* to connect reasons to their opinion. Have children use text evidence to support their reasons.

Children's paragraphs should:

- state a clear opinion about the topic
- supply reasons for the opinion using examples from the text
- provide some sense of closure
- demonstrate strong command of the conventions of standard written English

Ⓒ **Common Core State Standards**

Writing 1. Write opinion pieces in which they introduce the topic or book they are writing about, state an opinion, supply reasons that support the opinion, use linking words (e.g., because, and, also) to connect opinion and reasons, and provide a concluding statement or section.

Connect the Texts

Argument: Paragraph

Student Prompt Review *Grace for President* and "Home Sweet Home." Both selections mention leaders but take place in different times, or settings. In which setting do you think it would be more difficult to be a leader? State your opinion in a brief paragraph and use details and evidence from the selections to support your opinion.

_____

_____

_____

_____

_____

_____

_____

_____

_____

_____

_____

_____

_____

_____

_____

Connect the Texts
Argumentative Paragraph

Student Prompt, p. 184 Review *Grace for President* and "Home Sweet Home." Both selections mention leaders but take place in different times, or settings. In which setting do you think it would be more difficult to be a leader? State your opinion in a brief paragraph and use details and evidence from the selections to support your opinion.

Writing to Sources Review both selections with children. Tell them the two selections tell about very different times in history. Discuss the differences in the settings with children. Then ask children to write their opinion about which time period they think would be more difficult in which to be a leader. Have them give reasons using details and evidence from the selections to support their opinion.

		4-point Argument Writing Rubric			
Score	**Statement of Purpose/Focus**	**Organization**	**Development of Evidence**	**Language and Vocabulary**	**Conventions**
4	Opinion is clearly conveyed and well supported; response is focused.	Organization is clear and effective, creating a sense of cohesion.	Evidence is thorough and persuasive, and includes facts and details.	Ideas are clearly and effectively conveyed, using precise language and/or domain-specific vocabulary.	Command of conventions is strongly demonstrated.
3	Opinion is clear, adequately supported; response is generally focused.	Organization is clear, though minor flaws may be present and some ideas may be disconnected.	Evidence is adequate and includes facts and details.	Ideas are adequately conveyed, using both precise and more general language; may include domain-specific vocabulary.	Command of conventions is sufficiently demonstrated.
2	Opinion is somewhat supported; response may lack focus or include unnecessary material.	Organization is inconsistent, and flaws are apparent.	Evidence is uneven or incomplete; insufficient use of facts and details.	Ideas are unevenly conveyed, using overly-simplistic language; lack of domain-specific vocabulary.	Command of conventions is uneven.
1	The response may be confusing, unfocused; opinion not sufficiently supported.	Organization is poor or nonexistent.	Evidence is poor or nonexistent.	Ideas are conveyed in a vague, unclear, or confusing manner.	There is very little command of conventions.
0	The response shows no evidence of the ability to construct a coherent opinion essay using information from sources.				

Common Core State Standards

Writing 1. Write opinion pieces in which they introduce the topic or book they are writing about, state an opinion, supply reasons that support the opinion, use linking words (e.g., because, and, also) to connect opinion and reasons, and provide a concluding statement or section.

Prove It!
Newspaper Column

An Exciting Job

Newspaper Column

Discuss with children times they have tried to persuade someone to agree with them. Point out how important good reasons are in persuading someone. Remind children of texts and writing tasks (such as Write Like a Reporter and Connect the Texts) in which they have encountered and practiced argument or persuasive writing.

Key Features of a Newspaper Column

- states an opinion about the topic clearly
- gives reasons for the opinion and supports the reasons with facts and details
- organizes the reasons in a logical order
- includes words to link the opinion to the reasons (*because, and, for example*)
- uses persuasive words such as *best, important,* and *should* to convince readers to agree
- provides a concluding statement that summarizes the main point

Writing Task Overview

Each unit writing task provides children with an opportunity to write to sources. To successfully complete the task, children must analyze, synthesize, and evaluate multiple complex texts and create their own written response.

An Exciting Job

Part 1: Children will reread the selections identified from this unit. They will then respond to questions about these sources and discuss their written responses with partners.

Part 2: Children will work individually to plan, write, and revise their own newspaper column.

Scorable Products: evidence-based short responses, newspaper column

An Exciting Job: Writing Task – Short Response

Teacher Directions:

1. Introduce the Sources Refer children to the following texts in the Student Edition:

1. *Cowboys* pp. 466–487

2. *Grace for President* pp. 504–519

Explain to children that they will need to find information in these texts to answer questions. Tell children that they will also write their own newspaper columns using information from the texts.

2. Provide Directions (pp. 190–191) Answer any task-related questions children may have.

3. Facilitate Collaboration After children have completed their written responses to the evidence-based short response questions, assign partners or small groups and have them discuss their responses. If children struggle to work together productively, provide them with tips and strategies for expressing their ideas and building on others'.

Ⓒ **Common Core State Standards**

Writing 1. Write opinion pieces in which they introduce the topic or book they are writing about, state an opinion, supply reasons that support the opinion, use linking words (e.g., because, and, also) to connect opinion and reasons, and provide a concluding statement or section.

Scoring Information

Use the following 2-point scoring rubrics to evaluate children's answers to the evidence-based short response questions.

1. Each selection tells about one type of work. What are the skills and abilities needed to succeed at each job? Is the job tougher on the body or on the mind?

	Analysis Rubric	
2	The response: • demonstrates the ability to identify, analyze, and compare activity-specific skills, abilities, and demands across the texts • includes specific details that make reference to the texts	
1	The response: • demonstrates a limited ability to identify, analyze, and compare activity-specific skills, abilities, and demands across the texts • includes some details that make reference to the texts	
0	A response receives no credit if it demonstrates no ability to identify, analyze, and compare activity-specific skills, abilities, and demands across the texts or includes no relevant details from the texts.	

2. What do you think would prevent a person from being a cowboy or the President?

Synthesis Rubric	
2	The response: • demonstrates the ability to evaluate texts and synthesize information in order to conclude what limits a person's success • includes specific details that make reference to the texts
1	The response: • demonstrates a limited ability to evaluate texts and synthesize information in order to conclude what limits a person's success • includes some details that make reference to the texts
0	A response receives no credit if it demonstrates no ability to evaluate and synthesize information from the sources or includes no relevant details from the texts.

Ⓒ **Common Core State Standards**

Writing 1. Write opinion pieces in which they introduce the topic or book they are writing about, state an opinion, supply reasons that support the opinion, use linking words (e.g., because, and, also) to connect opinion and reasons, and provide a concluding statement or section.

An Exciting Job

Writing Task – Short Response

I. Each selection tells about one type of work. What are the skills and abilities needed to succeed at each job? Is the job tougher on the body or on the mind?

_____

_____

_____

_____

_____

_____

_____

_____

_____

_____

_____

2. What do you think would prevent a person from being a cowboy or the President?

_____

- -

_____

- -

_____

- -

_____

- -

_____

- -

_____

- -

_____

- -

_____

- -

_____

- -

_____

An Exciting Job: Writing Task – Newspaper Column

Teacher Directions:

1. **Provide Directions (p. 194)** Explain to children that they will now review the sources and plan, draft, and revise their newspaper columns. Children will be allowed to look back at the answers they wrote to the short response questions. Read aloud the directions for the newspaper column and answer any task-related questions they may have. Children should be given paper on which to write their newspaper columns.

2. **Scoring Information** Use the scoring rubric on the next page to evaluate children's newspaper columns.

3. **Newspaper Column Prompt** Use what you have learned from reading *Cowboys* and *Grace for President* to write a column for the school newspaper on the following topic: Being _____ would be an exciting job. Fill in the blank with *a cowboy* or *the President*.

What fun things would a cowboy/the President do?

What hard jobs would a cowboy/the President have to do?

How do you think the job would make you feel by the end of the day?

4-Point Argument Writing Rubric					
Score	Statement of Purpose/Focus	Organization	Development of Evidence	Language and Vocabulary	Conventions
4	Opinion is clearly stated and well supported in column.	Column contains reasons in a logical order and a conclusion.	Column includes sufficient evidence including facts and details.	Column uses linking and persuasive words effectively.	Column has correct grammar, usage, spelling, capitalization, and punctuation.
3	Opinion is clear and adequately supported in column.	Column's reasons are adequately organized.	Column includes adequate evidence including facts and details.	Column uses some linking and persuasive words.	Column has a few errors but is understandable.
2	Opinion is somewhat supported in column.	Column's organization is inconsistent.	Column's evidence is insufficient.	Column uses few linking or persuasive words.	Column has some errors in usage, grammar, spelling, and/or punctuation.
1	Column lacks opinion and/or support.	Column lacks organization.	Column lacks evidence.	Column's language is vague or confusing.	Column is hard to follow because of numerous errors.
0	Newspaper column receives no credit if it does not demonstrate adequate command of argument or persuasive writing traits.				

© Common Core State Standards

Writing 1. Write opinion pieces in which they introduce the topic or book they are writing about, state an opinion, supply reasons that support the opinion, use linking words (e.g., because, and, also) to connect opinion and reasons, and provide a concluding statement or section.

Name _____

An Exciting Job

Writing Task – Newspaper Column

Newspaper Column Prompt

Use what you have learned from reading *Cowboys* and *Grace for President* to write a column for the school newspaper on the following topic: Being _____ would be an exciting job. Fill in the blank with *a cowboy* or *the President*.

What fun things would a cowboy/the President do?

_____

_____

What hard jobs would a cowboy/the President have to do?

_____

_____

How do you think the job would make you feel by the end of the day?

_____

_____

An Exciting Job: Writing Task – Newspaper Column

Teacher Directions:

1. Publish Explain to children that publishing their writing is the last step in the writing process. If time permits, have children review one another's compositions and incorporate any comments their classmates have. Discuss different ways technology can be used to publish writing.

2. Present Children will now have the option to present their newspaper columns. Have children read aloud their newspaper columns to the class. Use the list below to offer children tips on listening and speaking.

While Listening to a Classmate...

- Listen closely and ask yourself: "Is this reason true? Has it been proved?"
- Think about how the details and examples support the reasons.

While Speaking to Classmates...

- Have good posture and eye contact.
- Speak clearly, at an appropriate pace, and with persuasive expression.

Things to Do Together...

- Ask and answer questions about reasons.
- Build on each other's ideas.

ⓒ Common Core State Standards

Writing 1. Write opinion pieces in which they introduce the topic or book they are writing about, state an opinion, supply reasons that support the opinion, use linking words (e.g., because, and, also) to connect opinion and reasons, and provide a concluding statement or section.

More Connect the Texts

Persuasive Paragraph

STEP 1 Read Like a Writer

Review the key features of a persuasive paragraph listed below. Respond to any questions children might have.

Key Features of a Persuasive Paragraph

- States the writer's opinion about a topic
- Supports the opinion with details and examples
- Uses strong language to express opinions and persuade readers
- Often organizes reasons in order of importance
- Provides a concluding statement

Choose a persuasive paragraph or text that children have already read to model key features. Display the model for children to see and point out each of the key features you have discussed.

STEP 2 Organize Your Ideas

Writing Prompt Look back at *The Twin Club* and *Henry and Mudge and the Starry Night.* Both texts discuss fun outdoor activities that people can do in the summer. Write a persuasive paragraph about which outdoor activity from the stories is your favorite and why. Support your opinion with facts, details, and examples from the texts.

Think Aloud Your ideas will be more convincing if they are well organized. Decide on the opinion, or claim, you will state in your persuasive paragraph. Make a list of reasons this activity appeals to you. Then look for details and examples from the texts you can use to support your opinion.

Guided Writing Assist children with their lists. Help them decide on the three strongest reasons for their opinion. Tell them to review *The Twin Club* and *Henry and Mudge and the Starry Night* to see if there are any pertinent details they can use from the featured selections.

Objectives

- Identify the characteristics of a persuasive paragraph.
- Write a persuasive paragraph, using supporting details.
- Evaluate your writing.
- Revise and publish your writing.

© Common Core State Standards

Writing 1. Write opinion pieces in which they introduce the topic or book they are writing about, state an opinion, supply reasons that support the opinion, use linking words (e.g., *because, and, also*) to connect opinion and reasons, and provide a concluding statement or section.

STEP 3 Draft Your Writing

Have children use their lists to write a persuasive paragraph. Remind them of the key features of a persuasive paragraph.

Think Aloud One of the best ways to express your opinion is to list details and examples that support your opinion. First, state your opinion clearly. Try to think of specific reasons why you feel the way you do. Then look for additional details from *The Twin Club* and *Henry and Mudge and the Starry Night.*

Getting Started Tell children to begin writing their persuasive paragraphs using their lists to keep them on track. Give them suggestions on how to organize their reasons with details and examples. Emphasize the importance of using correct grammar and complete sentences. Remind children to end their paragraphs with a concluding statement.

STEP 4 Evaluate Your Writing

Display the checklist below and have children use it to evaluate their persuasive paragraphs. Circulate around the room and confer with individual children.

✓ Did I introduce my topic at the beginning?

✓ Did I state my opinion clearly?

✓ Do my reasons support my opinion?

✓ Did I use strong words to make my writing more persuasive?

✓ Does my concluding statement make sense?

Help children set goals and make a plan for improving in areas where their writing needs help.

STEP 5 Revise and Publish

Help children follow through with their plans for revision. If time permits, have children trade persuasive paragraphs and offer suggestions for how to improve the writing.

Publishing Collect the persuasive paragraphs and put them in a classroom book.

Persuasive Letter

Objectives

- Identify the characteristics of a persuasive letter.
- Write a persuasive letter using facts and supporting details.
- Evaluate your writing.
- Revise and publish your writing.

Ⓒ Common Core State Standards

Writing 1. Write opinion pieces in which they introduce the topic or book they are writing about, state an opinion, supply reasons that support the opinion, use linking words (e.g., *because, and, also*) to connect opinion and reasons, and provide a concluding statement or section.

STEP 1 Read Like a Writer

Review the key features of a persuasive letter listed below. Respond to any questions children might have.

Key Features of a Persuasive Letter
- States the writer's opinion about a topic
- Supports the opinion with reasons, facts, and examples
- Uses persuasive words such as *most* and *best*
- Often organizes reasons in order of importance
- Provides a concluding statement
- Uses correct letter format and conventions

Choose a persuasive text or letter that children have already read to model key features. Display the model for children to see and point out each of the key features you have discussed.

STEP 2 Organize Your Ideas

Writing Prompt Look back at *Exploring Space with an Astronaut* and "A Trip to Space Camp." Both texts discuss the skills required to be an astronaut. Write a persuasive letter that tells what you think are the most important things a young person can do to prepare to be an astronaut. Write the letter to a family member, friend, or teacher. Persuade the person to agree with your ideas. Support your opinion with facts and details from both texts. Include persuasive words such as *need, important,* and *should.*

Think Aloud Your ideas will be more convincing if they are well organized. Decide on the opinion, or claim, you will state in your letter. Then decide what facts, details, and examples from the texts you will use to support your opinion. You may wish to fill in a chart before you begin writing.

Guided Writing Display a chart with four boxes as an example. Show children how to write their opinion in the first box and then write the ideas that support their opinion in the other three boxes. Explain to them that when they write, they will first state their opinion, then arrange their reasons in a logical order, and finally end with a statement that sums up their opinion.

STEP 3 Draft Your Writing

Have children use their charts to write a persuasive letter. Remind them of the key features of a persuasive letter.

Think Aloud One of the best ways to persuade readers is to use facts and details that support your opinion. You can find facts and details to support your opinion by rereading *Exploring Space with an Astronaut* and "A Trip to Space Camp."

Getting Started Tell children to begin writing their persuasive letter using their charts to keep them on track. Give them suggestions on how to organize their reasons with supporting facts and details from the texts.

STEP 4 Evaluate Your Writing

Display the checklist below and have children use it to evaluate their persuasive letters. Circulate around the room and confer with individual children.

✓ Did I introduce my topic at the beginning?

✓ Did I state my opinion clearly?

✓ Do my reasons support my opinion?

✓ Did I use persuasive words to make my writing more convincing?

✓ Does my concluding statement make sense?

✓ Did I use correct letter format and conventions?

Help children set goals and make a plan for improving in areas where their writing needs help.

STEP 5 Revise and Publish

Help children follow through with their plans for revision. If time permits, have children trade persuasive letters and offer suggestions for how to improve the writing.

Publishing Children can publish their letter by presenting it to the person to whom it is addressed.

More Connect the Texts
Review

Objectives

- Identify the characteristics of a literature review.
- Write a literature review, supporting the opinions with details and examples.
- Evaluate your writing.
- Revise and publish your writing.

Ⓒ Common Core State Standards

Writing 1. Write opinion pieces in which they introduce the topic or book they are writing about, state an opinion, supply reasons that support the opinion, use linking words (e.g., *because, and, also*) to connect opinion and reasons, and provide a concluding statement or section.

STEP 1 Read Like a Writer

Review the key features of a review listed below. Respond to any questions children might have.

Key Features of a Review

- Tells what a selection is about
- Gives an opinion about the selection
- Often urges others to read, or avoid, the selection

Model key features by selecting a review children have already read or by creating your own brief example. Display the model for children to see and point out each of the key features you have discussed.

STEP 2 Organize Your Ideas

Writing Prompt Review *One Good Turn Deserves Another* and "The Lion and the Mouse." Both texts are folk tales. Write a review that tells what you like and dislike about each selection. Support your review with opinions and details from the texts. Tell why a person should, or should not, read these selections.

Think Aloud Think about each selection. Identify the characters, plot, and lesson from each story. List what you like and dislike about each selection. Then identify the story you prefer, and use details and examples from the texts to support your opinion.

Guided Writing Instruct children that both stories feature an animal that surprises the other with its actions. Both also offer a similar lesson: that one good turn deserves another. Have children discuss what they like and dislike about each story. Assist children in making their lists and adding facts and details from the texts.

STEP 3 Draft Your Writing

Have children use their lists to write a literature review. Remind them of the key features of a review.

Think Aloud Your review will be more effective when you include facts and details from the selection. When planning your review, revisit the selections to find facts and details to support your arguments and opinions.

Getting Started Tell children to begin writing their reviews. Give them suggestions on how to organize their reasons with supporting facts and details. Emphasize the importance of using correct grammar and complete sentences. Additionally, remind them to use persuasive terms to emphasize their points. Remind children to end their review with a concluding statement.

STEP 4 Evaluate Your Writing

Display the checklist below and have children use it to evaluate their literature reviews. Circulate around the room and confer with individual children.

- ✓ Did I state my opinion clearly?
- ✓ Did I summarize the selections with my likes and dislikes?
- ✓ Do my reasons support my opinion?
- ✓ Did I use persuasive words to make my writing more convincing?
- ✓ Did I finish with a strong conclusion?

Help children set goals and make a plan for improving in areas where their writing needs help.

STEP 5 Revise and Publish

Help children follow through with their plans for revision. If time permits, have children trade reviews and offer suggestions for how to improve the writing.

Publishing Children can present their reviews to the class. Encourage children to listen and offer constructive feedback.

More Connect the Texts
Advertisement

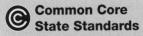
STEP 1 Read Like a Writer

Review the key features of an advertisement listed below. Respond to any questions children might have.

Key Features of an Advertisement

- Tries to influence the attitudes or actions of people
- Has information that is easy to read
- Often includes photos or illustrations
- Has a specific audience

Choose an advertisement to show children. Display the model for children to see and point out each of the key features you have discussed.

STEP 2 Organize Your Ideas

Writing Prompt Review *Scarcity* and "Goods and Services." The texts discuss goods that we buy and consume. Choose one of the goods or services from the selections. Write an advertisement for that good or service using evidence from the texts.

Think Aloud Look at different advertisements. Identify what the advertisements have in common. Recognize the words they use to describe the good or service. Look at the images that are included. Identify how they help sell the product.

Guided Writing With help from the class, list the goods and services that are in the selections. Then discuss facts and details about each one using evidence from the texts.

STEP 3 Draft Your Writing

Have children use examples of other advertisements as tools to help them. Remind them of the key features of an advertisement.

Think Aloud Your advertisement will be more effective when you include facts, details, and descriptive words about the good or service.

Getting Started Tell children to begin writing their advertisements. Give them suggestions on possible slogans. Emphasize the importance of using persuasive words to draw in the reader.

STEP 4 Evaluate Your Writing

Display the checklist below and have children use it to evaluate their advertisements. Circulate around the room and confer with individual children.

- ✓ Is it clear what my product is?
- ✓ Did I use appropriate facts and details about the product?
- ✓ Did I use persuasive words to make my writing more convincing?
- ✓ Did I include appropriate images of my product?

Help children set goals and make a plan for improving in areas where their writing needs help.

STEP 5 Revise and Publish

Help children follow through with their plans for revision. If time permits, have children trade advertisements and offer suggestions for how to improve the writing.

Publishing Have children illustrate their advertisements. Then have them place their written advertisements and illustrations on poster board.

More Connect the Texts
Review

STEP 1 Read Like a Writer

Review the key features of a review listed below. Respond to any questions children might have.

Key Features of a Review
- Introduces a selection
- States the writer's opinion of the selection
- Describes what the writer likes or doesn't like about the text
- Uses reasons and details from the text to support the opinion
- Uses persuasive words such as *important, best,* and *most*
- Provides a concluding statement

Choose a review that children have already read to model key features. Display the model for children to see and point out each of the key features you have discussed.

STEP 2 Organize Your Ideas

Writing Prompt Return to the selections *Pearl and Wagner: Two Good Friends* and "The Crow and the Pitcher." Each story has a message or lesson for the reader. Write a review of each selection. Tell what you liked most about each selection. Explain which story you think has the most important lesson and why. Use details from both texts to support your opinion.

Think Aloud You will begin your review by explaining what each story is about. Who are the characters? What is the plot? Think about the message or lesson of each story. Pearl and Wagner show that it is important for friends to help each other. The crow shows that not giving up can help solve a problem. Express a clear opinion about what you liked most about each story and which story has the most important lesson. Be sure to explain why, using reasons supported by details from both texts. Plan and organize your thoughts before writing. You want to be sure your writing answers the entire prompt.

Guided Writing Tell children that they will explain what they liked best about each story in separate paragraphs. They will express their opinion about what is the most important lesson in their final paragraph. Guide children in organizing their ideas. Have them take notes on what they liked best about each selection. Then ask children to jot notes of their opinion on the most important lesson. Remind them to supply reasons for their opinions supported by text evidence. These notes will guide them as they draft.

STEP 3 Draft Your Writing

Have children use their notes to write a literature review. Remind them of the key features of a review.

Think Aloud When you write a literature review, you are expressing your ideas and opinions of what you have read. Using details from both texts to support your opinion will help you convince readers to agree with you. Use words such as *important, best,* and *most* when supporting your opinion. These are strong words that help persuade the reader. Write up your thoughts with a concluding statement.

Getting Started Tell children to begin writing their literature review referring to their notes as a guide. Instruct them to use words such as *because* to connect their opinion and reasons. If necessary, help children locate text evidence to support their opinions. Explain to children the importance of using complete sentences and correct grammar.

STEP 4 Evaluate Your Writing

Display the checklist below and have children use it to evaluate their literature review. Circulate around the room and confer with individual children.

- ✓ Did I introduce the selections?
- ✓ Did I tell what I liked most about each selection?
- ✓ Did I tell what lesson I thought is most important?
- ✓ Are my opinions clear?
- ✓ Did I use reasons and details from both selections to support my opinions?
- ✓ Did I use persuasive words?
- ✓ Does my concluding statement make sense?

Help children set goals and make a plan for improving in areas where their writing needs work.

STEP 5 Revise and Publish

Help children follow through with their plans for revision. If time permits, have children trade literature reviews and offer advice on how to improve the writing.

Publishing Children can publish their review by including illustrations in their final draft. Combine children's work into a class book of reviews. Display it in the classroom in a place where children can access and read it.

More Connect the Texts
Persuasive Essay

Objectives

- Identify the characteristics of a persuasive essay.
- Write a persuasive essay, using supporting details and text evidence.
- Evaluate your writing.
- Revise and publish your writing.

Common Core State Standards

Writing 1. Write opinion pieces in which they introduce the topic or book they are writing about, state an opinion, supply reasons that support the opinion, use linking words (e.g., *because, and, also*) to connect opinion and reasons, and provide a concluding statement or section.

STEP 1 Read Like a Writer

Review the key features of a persuasive essay listed below. Respond to any questions children might have.

Key Features of a Persuasive Essay

- Offers an opinion about something
- Tries to persuade the reader to believe or do something
- Uses details and reasons to support the opinion
- Uses persuasive words to help convince the reader to take action
- Provides a concluding statement

Choose a persuasive essay that children have already read to model key features. You could also create your own example. Display the model for children to see and point out each of the key features you have discussed.

STEP 2 Organize Your Ideas

Writing Prompt *A Weed Is a Flower* and "Alberto, the Scientist" are about science and scientists. Look back at George Washington Carver and Alberto and what they were able to do by studying science. Think about why science is important. Write a persuasive essay to convince your classmates to spend more time studying science outside of school. Use details from both selections to support your opinion.

Think Aloud Review *A Weed Is a Flower* and "Alberto, the Scientist." What are some things Alberto learned about the world through science? How did Carver help others through science? There are many details in each selection you could use in your persuasive essay. Not every detail helps you make your case, though. For example, telling that Carver was born in 1860 will not help you convince others to study science. Choose only the details that support your opinion.

Guided Writing Assist children as they gather text evidence for their persuasive essay. Explain that when they draft their writing, they will include a sentence that clearly tries to convince the reader to study science. The other sentences will present reasons and details from both selections to support this opinion.

STEP 3 Draft Your Writing

Have children draw upon the text evidence they've gathered to write a persuasive statement. Remind them of the key features of a persuasive essay.

Think Aloud Remember that you are asking your readers to take action. Persuasive words will help you convince others to spend more time studying science. Use words such as *must, should,* and *need* in your writing. Don't forget to write a concluding statement at the end of your essay to sum up your thoughts.

Getting Started As children begin writing their persuasive essay, remind them to include persuasive words. If necessary, offer suggestions on where to replace a weak word with a stronger, more persuasive one. Remind children to include supporting details from each selection. Ask children to check their writing for complete sentences and correct grammar and conventions.

STEP 4 Evaluate Your Writing

Display the checklist below and have children use it to evaluate their persuasive essays. Circulate around the room and confer with individual children.

- ✓ Did I try to persuade the reader to believe or do something?
- ✓ Did I use details and reasons to support my opinion that others should spend more time studying science?
- ✓ Did I use persuasive words?
- ✓ Did I provide a strong concluding statement?
- ✓ Did I use correct grammar and conventions?

Help children set goals and make a plan for improving in areas where their writing needs more attention.

STEP 5 Revise and Publish

Help children follow through with their plans for revision. If time permits, have children trade persuasive essays and offer feedback on how to improve the writing.

Publishing Children can read their persuasive statement to the class. Ask listeners to share the reason they thought was most convincing.

More Connect the Texts
Review

Objectives

- Identify the characteristics of a literature review.
- Write a literature review, supporting the opinions with details and examples.
- Evaluate your writing.
- Revise and publish your writing.

© Common Core State Standards

Writing 1. Write opinion pieces in which they introduce the topic or book they are writing about, state an opinion, supply reasons that support the opinion, use linking words (e.g., *because, and, also*) to connect opinion and reasons, and provide a concluding statement or section.

STEP 1 Read Like a Writer

Review the key features of a review listed below. Respond to any questions children might have.

Key Features of a Review

- Tells what a selection is about
- Gives an opinion about the selection
- Often urges others to read, or avoid, the selection

Model key features by selecting a review children have already read or by creating your own brief example. Display the model for children to see and point out each of the key features you have discussed.

STEP 2 Organize Your Ideas

Writing Prompt Review *The Night the Moon Fell* and *The First Tortilla*. One story is a myth and the other is a legend, so both deal with characters that are not real. Write a review that tells what you like and dislike about each selection. Support your review with opinions and details from the texts. Tell why a person should, or should not, read these selections.

Think Aloud Summarize each selection. Identify the characters, plot, and purpose of each story. Then tell how the stories are similar and different. Identify the story you prefer, and use details and examples from the texts to support your opinion.

Guided Writing Assist children in summarizing each story. Instruct them that both stories attempt to explain something in the natural world. Explain to children that people would make up these kinds of stories as a way to make sense of things they did not understand.

STEP 3 Draft Your Writing

Have children use their summaries to write a literature review. Remind them of the key features of a review.

Think Aloud Your review will be more effective when you include facts and details from the selection. When planning your review, revisit the selections to find facts and details to support your arguments and opinions.

Getting Started Tell children to begin writing their reviews. Give them suggestions on how to organize their reasons with supporting facts and details. Remind children to use persuasive words to emphasize their points. Instruct them to end their review with a concluding statement.

STEP 4 Evaluate Your Writing

Display the checklist below and have children use it to evaluate their literature reviews. Circulate around the room and confer with individual children.

- ✓ Did I state my opinion clearly?
- ✓ Did I accurately summarize the selections?
- ✓ Do my reasons support my opinion?
- ✓ Did I use persuasive words to make my writing more convincing?
- ✓ Did I finish with a strong conclusion?

Help children set goals and make a plan for improving in areas where their writing needs help.

STEP 5 Revise and Publish

Help children follow through with their plans for revision. If time permits, have children trade reviews and offer suggestions for how to improve the writing.

Publishing Children can present their reviews to the class. Encourage children to listen and offer constructive feedback.

Persuasive Letter

Objectives

- Identify the characteristics of a persuasive letter.
- Write a persuasive letter, using facts and supporting details.
- Evaluate your writing.
- Revise and publish your writing.

© Common Core State Standards

Writing 1. Write opinion pieces in which they introduce the topic or book they are writing about, state an opinion, supply reasons that support the opinion, use linking words (e.g., *because, and, also*) to connect opinion and reasons, and provide a concluding statement or section.

STEP 1 Read Like a Writer

Review the key features of a persuasive letter listed below. Respond to any questions children might have.

Key Features of a Persuasive Letter

- States the writer's opinion about a topic
- Follows correct letter format
- Supports the opinion with reasons, facts, and examples
- Uses persuasive words such as *need, important,* and *should*
- Often organizes reasons in order of importance
- Provides a concluding statement
- Uses correct letter format and conventions

Choose an opinion piece or persuasive text that children have already read to model key features. Display the model for children to see and point out each of the key features you have discussed.

STEP 2 Organize Your Ideas

Writing Prompt Look back at *Life Cycle of a Pumpkin* and *Soil*. These texts teach us about the growing process of plants and fruit, as well as details about the soil that they grow in. Write a persuasive letter to a family member or teacher that tells what you think should be planted in your yard at home or at your school. Persuade the person to agree with your ideas. Support your opinion with facts and details from the texts. Include persuasive words such as *need, important,* and *should.*

Think Aloud Your ideas will be more convincing if they are well organized. Decide on the opinion, or claim, you will state in your letter. Then decide what facts, details, and examples from the texts you will use to support your opinion. You may wish to fill in a chart before you begin writing.

Guided Writing Display a four-box chart as an example. Show children how to write their opinion in the first box and then write details and facts that support their opinion in the other boxes. Explain to them that when they write, they will first state their opinion, then arrange their reasons in a logical order, and end with a statement that sums up their opinion.

STEP 3 Draft Your Writing

Have children use their charts to write a persuasive letter. Remind them of the key features of a persuasive letter.

Think Aloud Remember that a persuasive letter follows correct letter format. It should state your opinion and includes facts and details from the texts to help convince the person who will read your letter to agree with you.

Getting Started Tell children to begin writing their persuasive letter using their charts to keep them on track. Give them suggestions on how to organize their reasons with supporting facts and details. Emphasize the importance of using correct grammar and complete sentences. Remind children to end their letter with a concluding statement.

STEP 4 Evaluate Your Writing

Display the checklist below and have children use it to evaluate their persuasive letters. Circulate around the room and confer with individual children.

- ✓ Did I introduce my topic at the beginning?
- ✓ Did I state my opinion clearly?
- ✓ Do my reasons support my opinion?
- ✓ Did I use persuasive words to make my writing more convincing?
- ✓ Does my concluding statement make sense?
- ✓ Did I use correct letter format and conventions?

Help children set goals and make a plan for improving in areas where their writing needs help.

STEP 5 Revise and Publish

Help children follow through with their plans for revision. If time permits, have children trade persuasive letters and offer suggestions for how to improve the writing.

Publishing Children can publish their letter by presenting it to the person to whom it is addressed.

More Connect the Texts
Persuasive Essay

Objectives

- Identify the characteristics of a persuasive essay.
- Write a persuasive essay, using facts and supporting details.
- Evaluate your writing.
- Revise and publish your writing.

© Common Core State Standards

Writing 1. Write opinion pieces in which they introduce the topic or book they are writing about, state an opinion, supply reasons that support the opinion, use linking words (e.g., *because, and, also*) to connect opinion and reasons, and provide a concluding statement or section.

STEP 1 Read Like a Writer

Review the key features of a persuasive essay listed below. Respond to any questions children might have.

Key Features of a Persuasive Essay
- Introduces the topic
- Takes a position on a subject
- Provides details to support the position
- May urge the reader to take action
- Uses persuasive words
- Provides a strong conclusion

Select an opinion piece or persuasive text that children have already read to model key features. Display the model for children to see and point out each of the key features you have discussed.

STEP 2 Organize Your Ideas

Writing Prompt Look back at *Carl the Complainer* and "Helping Hand." These texts are about people who help out in their community. Write a persuasive essay that tells why it is important to be a community helper. Suggest ways people can make their towns and neighborhoods better places to live. Support your position with facts and details from the two selections.

Think Aloud Your essays will be more effective if they are well organized. Choose the reasons you will use to support your topic. Then decide what facts, details, and examples from the texts you will use to support your position. You may wish to use a list to organize your main points and supporting details.

Guided Writing List the following: *main idea, reason 1, example, reason 2, example.* Explain how this pattern represents a simple way to organize a persuasive essay. Tell children that when they write, they will first state their opinion and then arrange reasons in a logical order, supported by examples, facts, and details from the texts.

STEP 3 Draft Your Writing

Have children use their lists to write a persuasive essay. Remind them of the key features of a persuasive essay.

Think Aloud A good technique when writing a persuasive essay is to use persuasive language. Support your writing with words such as *important, urgent, best, help, strong,* and *great.* These words can help entice readers to think and act a certain way. You can use a thesaurus to identify more persuasive words and phrases.

Getting Started Tell children to begin writing their persuasive essay using their lists and notes. Remind them to remain focused on their main topic and to support each idea with examples and details from *Carl the Complainer* and "Helping Hand." Emphasize that a persuasive essay should reinforce the topic with a strong conclusion that restates the main topic.

STEP 4 Evaluate Your Writing

Display the checklist below and have children use it to evaluate their persuasive essays. Circulate around the room and confer with individual children.

- ✓ Did I introduce my topic at the beginning?
- ✓ Did I state my position clearly?
- ✓ Do my reasons support my position?
- ✓ Did I urge readers to take action?
- ✓ Did I use persuasive words to make my writing more convincing?
- ✓ Did I use a strong concluding statement?

Help children set goals and make a plan for improving in areas where their writing needs help.

STEP 5 Revise and Publish

Help children follow through with their plans for revision. If time permits, have children trade persuasive essays and offer suggestions for how to improve the writing.

Publishing Children can publish their essays by including a persuasive poster that urges people to get involved in their communities.

Persuasive Essay

Objectives

- Identify the characteristics of a persuasive essay.
- Write a persuasive essay using facts and supporting details.
- Evaluate your writing.
- Revise and publish your writing.

Common Core State Standards

Writing 1. Write opinion pieces in which they introduce the topic or book they are writing about, state an opinion, supply reasons that support the opinion, use linking words (e.g., *because, and, also*) to connect opinion and reasons, and provide a concluding statement or section.

STEP 1 Read Like a Writer

Review the key features of a persuasive essay listed below. Respond to any questions children might have.

Key Features of a Persuasive Essay

- Clearly states an opinion
- Gives reasons that support the opinion
- Uses linking words to connect opinion and reasons
- Provides a strong conclusion that restates the opinion

Model key features by selecting a persuasive essay or text. Display the model for children to see and point out each of the key features you have discussed.

STEP 2 Organize Your Ideas

Writing Prompt Review *Fire Fighter!* and "Firefighting Teamwork." Both texts are about firefighters. Write a persuasive essay that will convince someone how important firefighters are. Support your opinion with facts and details from both texts.

Think Aloud Plan and organize your persuasive essay to make it clear and effective. Decide what facts, details, and examples from the texts you will use to support your opinion. Make a T-chart as a guide.

Guided Writing Show children how to make and use a T-chart to organize their thoughts. Make a T-chart for each selection. You may choose to use your model review to fill in the T-chart with facts and details to support an opinion. Have children help you fill in the chart. Then tell children they will use a T-chart to organize their own writing.

STEP 3 Draft Your Writing

Have children use their T-charts to write a persuasive essay. Remind them of the key features of a persuasive essay.

Think Aloud Your persuasive essay will be better when you include facts and details from both texts. When planning your essay, revisit the selections to find facts and details to support your argument, or opinion.

Getting Started Tell children to begin writing their persuasive essays using their T-charts as a guide. Remind them to begin with a statement of opinion and follow with a reason and examples from the text. Emphasize the importance of using correct grammar and complete sentences. Remind children to end their persuasive essay with a concluding statement that restates their opinion.

STEP 4 Evaluate Your Writing

Display the checklist below and have children use it to evaluate their persuasive essays. Circulate around the room and confer with individual children.

- ✓ Did I introduce my topic at the beginning?
- ✓ Did I state my opinion clearly?
- ✓ Do my reasons support my opinion?
- ✓ Did I use linking words to connect opinions and reasons?
- ✓ Does my concluding statement make sense?

Help children set goals and make a plan for improving in areas where their writing needs help.

STEP 5 Revise and Publish

Help children follow through with their plans for revision. If time permits, have children trade their persuasive essays and offer suggestions for how to improve the writing.

Publishing Children can share their essays by compiling them into a class book to share.

Persuasive Paragraph

Objectives

- Identify the characteristics of a persuasive paragraph.
- Write a persuasive paragraph, using facts and supporting details.
- Evaluate your writing.
- Revise and publish your writing.

Ⓒ Common Core State Standards

Writing 1. Write opinion pieces in which they introduce the topic or book they are writing about, state an opinion, supply reasons that support the opinion, use linking words (e.g., *because, and, also*) to connect opinion and reasons, and provide a concluding statement or section.

STEP 1 Read Like a Writer

Review the key features of a persuasive paragraph listed below. Respond to any questions children might have.

Key Features of a Persuasive Paragraph

- Introduces the topic
- Takes a position on a subject
- Provides reasons to support the position
- Uses persuasive words
- Provides a strong conclusion

Select a persuasive text that children have already read to model key features. Display the model for children to see and point out each of the key features you have discussed.

STEP 2 Organize Your Ideas

Writing Prompt Look back at *A Birthday Basket for Tía* and "Family Traditions: Birthdays." These texts are about birthdays. Write an opinion piece that tells why birthdays are important to people around the world. Support your position with facts and details from the two selections.

Think Aloud Your writing will be more effective if it is well organized. Choose the claim, or opinion, you will make to begin. Then decide what facts and details from the texts you will use to support your opinion.

Guided Writing List the following: *main point, reason, example, detail from text.* Explain how this pattern represents one way to organize text in a persuasive paragraph. Be sure children remember that each sentence in a paragraph must tell about their opinion and be in an order that makes sense.

STEP 3 Draft Your Writing

Have children begin drafting their persuasive paragraphs. Remind them of the key features of an opinion piece.

Think Aloud Support your writing with words such as *best, most, happiest,* and *great.* These words help the reader know how you feel and make your opinion clear.

Getting Started Encourage children to recall what you've discussed about organization and to begin writing their persuasive paragraph. Remind them to remain focused on their claim, or opinion, and to support it with examples and details from *A Birthday Basket for Tía* and "Family Traditions: Birthdays." Emphasize that a persuasive paragraph should reinforce the topic with a conclusion that restates your claim, or opinion.

STEP 4 Evaluate Your Writing

Display the checklist below and have children use it to evaluate their persuasive paragraphs. Circulate around the room and confer with individual children.

- ✓ Did I introduce my topic at the beginning?
- ✓ Did I state my position clearly?
- ✓ Do my reasons support my position?
- ✓ Did I use persuasive words to make my writing more convincing?
- ✓ Does my conclusion make sense?

Help children set goals and make a plan for improving in areas where their writing needs help.

STEP 5 Revise and Publish

Help children follow through with their plans for revision. If time permits, have children trade opinion pieces and offer suggestions for how to improve the writing.

Publishing Children can publish their persuasive paragraphs by including a picture or photograph from a favorite birthday celebration of their own.

More Connect the Texts
Review

Objectives

- Identify the characteristics of a review.
- Write a review using facts and supporting details.
- Evaluate your writing.
- Revise and publish your writing.

Common Core State Standards

Writing 1. Write opinion pieces in which they introduce the topic or book they are writing about, state an opinion, supply reasons that support the opinion, use linking words (e.g., *because, and, also*) to connect opinion and reasons, and provide a concluding statement or section.

STEP 1 Read Like a Writer

Review the key features of a review listed below. Respond to any questions children might have.

Key Features of a Review
- Introduces the selection
- Gives an opinion about the selection
- Gives reasons that support the opinion
- Uses linking words to connect opinion and reasons
- Often urges others to read the selection
- Provides a strong conclusion

Model key features by selecting a review children have already read or using another piece of argument writing. Display the model for children to see and point out each of the key features you have discussed.

STEP 2 Organize Your Ideas

Writing Prompt Take a closer look at *Just Like Josh Gibson* and *Grace for President.* Both stories are about a girl who wants to do something that boys do. Write a review that tells what you like and dislike about each selection. Tell why a person should or should not read these stories. Support your opinions with details from each of the texts.

Think Aloud Plan your review carefully. Organize your ideas so they will be clear and convincing. Introduce and summarize the main points of each story. Tell what the selections have in common. Select details and examples from the texts that were most important to you. These will help you express how you feel about the stories and make your argument more effective.

Guided Writing Review *Just Like Josh Gibson* and *Grace for President* with children. Help children summarize each selection. Have them tell how the stories are similar and how they are different. Ask children to identify sections and ideas they most liked or disliked. Encourage them to take notes on these parts and use them to organize their reviews.

STEP 3 Draft Your Writing

Have children use their notes to write a review. Remind them of the key features of a review.

Think Aloud Remember that proper organization is important to writing a good review. Make your statement first. Then supply examples and details to support the statement. Using linking words such as *because* and *also* can connect your opinions and reasons.

Getting Started Tell children to begin writing their reviews using their notes as a guide. Remind them to begin with a statement of opinion and follow with a reason and examples from the text. Emphasize the importance of using linking words, proper mechanics, and complete sentences. Remind children to end their review with a strong concluding statement that restates how they feel about the selections.

STEP 4 Evaluate Your Writing

Display the checklist below and have children use it to evaluate their reviews. Circulate around the room and confer with individual children.

✓ Did I introduce my topic at the beginning?

✓ Did I state my opinion clearly?

✓ Do my reasons support my opinion?

✓ Did I use linking words to connect opinions and reasons?

✓ Did I urge others to read the texts?

✓ Does my concluding statement make sense?

Help children set goals and make a plan for improving in areas where their writing needs help.

STEP 5 Revise and Publish

Help children follow through with their plans for revision. If time permits, have children trade reviews and offer suggestions for how to improve the writing.

Publishing Children can share their reviews by reading them aloud in small groups. After reviews have been shared, take a class vote on which selection children like better based on the reviews.

Persuasive Letter

Objectives

- Identify the characteristics of a persuasive letter.
- Write a persuasive letter, using facts and supporting details.
- Evaluate your writing.
- Revise and publish your writing.

© Common Core State Standards

Writing 1. Write opinion pieces in which they introduce the topic or book they are writing about, state an opinion, supply reasons that support the opinion, use linking words (e.g., *because, and, also*) to connect opinion and reasons, and provide a concluding statement or section.

STEP 1 Read Like a Writer

Review the key features of a persuasive letter listed below. Respond to any questions children might have.

Key Features of a Persuasive Letter

- States the writer's opinion about a topic
- Follows correct letter format
- Supports the opinion with reasons, facts, and examples
- Uses persuasive words, such as *most* and *best*
- Often organizes reasons in order of importance
- Provides a concluding statement
- Uses correct letter format and conventions

Choose an opinion piece or persuasive text that children have already read to model key features. Display the model for children to see and point out each of the key features you have discussed.

STEP 2 Organize Your Ideas

Writing Prompt Look back at *Cowboys* and "Cowboy Gear." These selections tell about the job of a cowboy. Write a persuasive letter that tells what you think are the most important things about the job of a cowboy. Write the letter to a friend, family member, or teacher. Persuade the person to agree with your ideas. Support your opinion with facts and details from both texts. Include persuasive words such as *best, need,* and *important.*

Think Aloud Your letter will be more convincing if it is well organized. Decide on the opinions you will state in your letter. Then decide what facts, details, and examples from the texts you will use to support your ideas. You can use a list to begin organizing your ideas.

Guided Writing On the board, write *First Idea.* Beneath this, make a three-point list with *facts and details* on each line. Show children how to write their opinion on the first line and then write the facts and details that support their opinion on the other three lines. Explain to them that when they write, they will first state their opinion, then arrange their reasons in a logical order, and finally end with a statement that sums up their opinion.

STEP 3 Draft Your Writing

Have children use their charts to write a persuasive letter. Remind them of the key features of a persuasive letter.

Think Aloud Remember that a persuasive letter follows correct letter format. Use facts and details from *Cowboys* and "Cowboy Gear" to support your opinion.

Getting Started Tell children to begin writing their persuasive letter using their lists as a guide. Remind them to use facts and details from the texts for support. Emphasize that children should end their letter with a concluding statement that restates their opinion.

STEP 4 Evaluate Your Writing

Display the checklist below and have children use it to evaluate their persuasive letters. Circulate around the room and confer with individual children.

✓ Did I introduce my topic at the beginning?

✓ Did I state my opinion clearly?

✓ Do my reasons support my opinion?

✓ Did I use persuasive words to make my writing more convincing?

✓ Does my concluding statement make sense?

✓ Did I use correct letter format and conventions?

Help children set goals and make a plan for improving in areas where their writing needs help.

STEP 5 Revise and Publish

Help children follow through with their plans for revision. If time permits, have children trade persuasive letters and offer suggestions for how to improve the writing.

Publishing Children can publish their letters by compiling them into a class book to share.

Compare and Contrast Essay

Objectives

- Identify the characteristics of a compare and contrast essay.
- Write a compare and contrast essay using facts and supporting details.
- Evaluate your writing.
- Revise and publish your writing.

Common Core State Standards

Writing 2. Write informative/explanatory texts in which they introduce a topic, use facts and definitions to develop points, and provide a concluding statement or section.

STEP 1 Read Like a Writer

Review the key features of a compare and contrast essay listed below. Respond to any questions children might have.

Key Features of a Compare and Contrast Essay

- Compares two things by telling how they are alike
- Contrasts two things by telling how they are different
- Uses compare and contrast words to point out likenesses and differences
- Uses facts and definitions to make points
- Provides a concluding statement

Choose a compare and contrast essay that children have already read to model key features. Display the model for children to see and point out each of the key features you have discussed.

STEP 2 Organize Your Ideas

Writing Prompt In *A Walk in the Desert* and "Rain Forests," you read about two different environments. Based on what you learned, compare and contrast these two environments. Provide evidence from the texts to support your points. Use precise words to point out how the environments are alike and different.

Think Aloud Your ideas will be more convincing if they are well organized. Think about all aspects of each environment: the temperature, precipitation, vegetation, and animal life. It can help to make a chart before you write. Label one side of the chart *Alike* and the other side *Different.*

Guided Writing Help children fill in their charts. Tell them that they will write one paragraph describing the likenesses and another paragraph describing the differences. Each paragraph will include facts and details that support the topic sentence.

STEP 3 Draft Your Writing

Have children use their charts to write a compare and contrast essay. Remind them of the key features of a compare and contrast essay.

Think Aloud It is important to include words that compare and contrast. Writers use these words to signal how things are alike or different. Common words that compare and contrast include *and, both, too, but, in contrast,* and *alike.*

Getting Started Tell children to begin writing their compare and contrast essay using their charts to keep them on track. Give them suggestions on where to place their facts and supporting details. Emphasize the importance of using correct grammar and complete sentences. Remind them to end with a concluding statement.

STEP 4 Evaluate Your Writing

Display the checklist below and have children use it to evaluate their compare and contrast essays. Circulate around the room and confer with individual children.

- ✓ Does the essay clearly compare and contrast two things?
- ✓ Are likenesses and differences clearly organized?
- ✓ Is it clear that I am interested in the topic?
- ✓ Does the essay use compare and contrast words?
- ✓ Are there words, phrases, or sentences that I could delete to make the essay less wordy?

Help children set goals and a plan for working on areas where their writing needs improvement.

STEP 5 Revise and Publish

Help children follow through with their plans for revision. If time permits, have children trade essays and offer up suggestions for how to improve the writing.

Publishing In their final draft, have children illustrate their essay with photographs or their own drawings.

Expository Text

Objectives

- Identify the characteristics of expository text.
- Write an expository text using facts and supporting details.
- Evaluate your writing.
- Revise and publish your writing.

Ⓒ Common Core State Standards

Writing 2. Write informative/explanatory texts in which they introduce a topic, use facts and definitions to develop points, and provide a concluding statement or section.

STEP 1 Read Like a Writer

Review the key features of an expository text listed below. Respond to any questions children might have.

Key Features of an Expository Text

- Explains an animal, place, object, or idea
- Gives facts and details about the topic
- Often includes text features, such as headings, and graphic features, such as pictures and maps

Choose an expository text that children have already read to model key features. Display the model for children to see and point out each of the key features you have discussed.

STEP 2 Organize Your Ideas

Writing Prompt The selection *The Strongest One* is about a little ant that tries to find out about strength. "Anteaters" is an expository text that provides excellent information about that animal. Explain how an anteater could be added to the story of *The Strongest One,* using evidence from both texts.

Think Aloud "Anteaters" provides us with a description of where anteaters live, what they look like, and what they eat. Make a chart with the headings *Where Anteaters Live, What Anteaters Look Like,* and *What Anteaters Eat.* List facts and details from "Anteaters" under each column.

Guided Writing Help children fill in their charts. Tell children that they can use the facts and details about anteaters to help them focus on explaining how an anteater could be added to *The Strongest One.*

STEP 3 Draft Your Writing

Have children use their charts to write their expository text. Remind them of the key features of expository text.

Think Aloud It is important to include graphic features in an expository text. Make sure to look for photos or images of your animal and where it lives to include in your final draft.

Getting Started Tell children to begin writing their expository text using their charts to keep them on track. Have them use *The Strongest One* and "Anteaters" for assistance on how to include facts and supporting details. Emphasize the importance of using correct grammar and complete sentences.

STEP 4 Evaluate Your Writing

Display the checklist below and have children use it to evaluate their expository texts. Circulate around the room and confer with individual children.

- ✓ Does the text clearly explain how an anteater could be added to *The Strongest One?*
- ✓ Are there clear details supporting the facts?
- ✓ Am I knowledgeable and informative on the topic?
- ✓ Are there words, phrases, or sentences that I could delete to make the text less wordy?

Help children set goals and a plan for working on areas where their writing needs improvement.

STEP 5 Revise and Publish

Help children follow through with their plans for revision. If time permits, have children trade expository texts and offer up suggestions for how to improve the writing.

Publishing In their final draft, make sure children include both text features and graphic features. Have children share their expository texts with the class.

More Connect the Texts
Summary

Objectives

- Identify the characteristics of a summary.
- Write a summary of the topic that includes all necessary information.
- Focus on organization/paragraphs.
- Revise and publish your writing.

Common Core State Standards

Writing 2. Write informative/explanatory texts in which they introduce a topic, use facts and definitions to develop points, and provide a concluding statement or section.

STEP 1 Read Like a Writer

Review the key features of a summary listed below. Respond to any questions children might have.

Key Features of a Summary

- Retells a piece or pieces of writing
- Includes only the most important information
- Is shorter than the original text
- Provides a concluding statement

Choose a summary that children have already read or create a simple sample to model key features. Display the model for children to see and point out each of the key features you have discussed.

STEP 2 Organize Your Ideas

Writing Prompt In *Abraham Lincoln* and "Lincoln," you learn about the life of Abraham Lincoln. Based on what you learned from these two sources, write a summary of his life. Provide evidence from the texts to support your points.

Think Aloud Your ideas will be more convincing if they are well organized. Think about the important things that happened to Lincoln when he was a boy and when he was a man. It can help to make a time line of the significant events.

Guided Writing Help children with their time lines. Ask them to identify only what they think are the most important things that happened in Lincoln's life.

STEP 3 Draft Your Writing

Have children use their time lines to write a summary. Remind them of the key features of a summary.

Think Aloud While the poem "Lincoln" does not specifically list the events in Lincoln's life, it still provides important clues that can be used in the summary. Look for descriptions of his youth, his character, and how the author refers to the later years of his life.

Getting Started Tell children to begin writing their summaries using their time lines to keep them on track. Give them suggestions on where to omit or include information. Emphasize the importance of using correct grammar and complete sentences. Instruct children to vary the beginnings of their sentences. Remind them to end with a concluding statement.

STEP 4 Evaluate Your Writing

Display the checklist below and have children use it to evaluate their summaries. Circulate around the room and confer with individual children.

    ✓ Is the summary clearly focused?

    ✓ Are there enough details?

    ✓ Is the summary clearly organized?

    ✓ Do my sentences begin with different words?

Help children set goals and a plan for working on areas where their writing needs improvement.

STEP 5 Revise and Publish

Help children follow through with their plans for revision. If time permits, have children trade summaries and offer suggestions for how to improve their writing.

Publishing Have children present their summaries to the class.

Expository Report

Objectives

- Develop an understanding of an expository report.
- Write an expository report.
- Provide facts and details about a topic.
- Establish criteria for evaluating a short expository report.

Ⓒ Common Core State Standards

Writing 2. Write informative/explanatory texts in which they introduce a topic, use facts and definitions to develop points, and provide a concluding statement or section.

STEP 1 Read Like a Writer

Review the key features of an expository report listed below. Respond to any questions children might have.

Key Features of an Expository Report
- Explains a person, animal, event, activity, idea, or object
- Gives facts and details about the topic
- Provides a concluding statement

Choose an expository text or paragraph that children have already read to model key features. Display the model for children to see and point out each of the key features you have discussed.

STEP 2 Organize Your Ideas

Writing Prompt In *Tara and Tiree, Fearless Friends* and "Rescue Dogs," you learn about some ways dogs help people. Based on what you learned from these two sources, as well as further research, write an expository report about the importance of dogs in people's lives. Provide evidence from the texts to support your points.

Think Aloud Your ideas will be more convincing if they are well organized. Making a list is an excellent way to organize information. Think of all the ways that dogs are useful in people's lives. Write them down. When you have finished, go through your list and choose the items you wish to include in your expository report.

Guided Writing Help children with their lists. When they have finished, have them choose the three most significant points to include in their reports. Explain that they will write a paragraph for each idea. Each paragraph will include facts and details that support the topic sentence.

STEP 3 Draft Your Writing

Have children use their lists to write an expository report. Remind them of the key features of a short expository report.

Think Aloud Remember that an expository report provides facts and details. You will use your lists as you write the draft of your report.

Getting Started Tell children to begin writing their short expository reports using their lists to keep them on track. Give them suggestions on where to use their facts and supporting details. Remind them to end with a concluding statement.

STEP 4 Evaluate Your Writing

Display the checklist below and have children use it to evaluate their short expository reports. Circulate around the room and confer with individual children.

- ✓ Are there enough details?
- ✓ Is the writer knowledgeable and informative?
- ✓ Is the short expository report clearly organized?
- ✓ Does the report include a strong conclusion?

Help children set goals and a plan for working on areas where their writing needs improvement.

STEP 5 Revise and Publish

Help children follow through with their plans for revision. If time permits, have children trade reports and offer suggestions for how to improve their writing.

Publishing In their final draft, have children include photos or illustrations. Encourage children to include captions with their images.

Compare and Contrast Essay

Objectives

- Identify the characteristics of a compare and contrast essay.
- Write a compare and contrast essay, using facts and supporting details.
- Organize ideas in an order that makes sense.
- Evaluate your writing.
- Revise and publish your writing.

Common Core State Standards

Writing 2. Write informative/explanatory texts in which they introduce a topic, use facts and definitions to develop points, and provide a concluding statement or section.

STEP 1 Read Like a Writer

Review the key features of a compare and contrast essay listed below. Respond to any questions children might have.

Key Features of a Compare and Contrast Essay

- Introduces a topic
- Compares two things by telling how they are alike
- Contrasts two things by telling how they are different
- Uses facts to explain points
- Uses clue words to explain likenesses and differences
- Provides a concluding statement

Choose a compare and contrast essay that children have already read to model key features. Display the model for children to see and point out each of the key features you have discussed.

STEP 2 Organize Your Ideas

Writing Prompt Look back at *Dear Juno* and *Rosa and Blanca*. Each selection is about a family. Think about Juno's family and Rosa and Blanca's family. How are they alike? How are they different? Write an essay to compare and contrast the families. Use clue words such as *alike* and *but* to explain the likenesses and differences. Be sure to use evidence from each text to support your points.

Think Aloud You must decide which likenesses and differences you will include in your essay. Organize your ideas before writing. A Venn diagram is a great tool to help you keep track of how each family is alike and different. Label the left section *Juno's Family,* the right section *Rosa and Blanca's Family,* and the middle section *Both Families.* Then review *Dear Juno* and *Rosa and Blanca* and find facts from each text to list in the diagram.

Guided Writing Assist children in completing their diagram. Explain that when they draft their essay, they should present their ideas in an order that makes sense. They should introduce the topic and draw evidence from both texts to support their points. They will present the likenesses in one paragraph and the differences in another paragraph. Referring to the points children listed in their Venn diagram will help them stay on track as they write.

STEP 3 Draft Your Writing

Have children use their Venn diagram to write a compare and contrast essay. Remind them of the key features of a compare and contrast essay.

Think Aloud When you compare and contrast two things, you must make it clear how they are alike and different. Clue words help a reader understand these likenesses and differences. Be sure to use words such as *both, all, unlike,* and *though* in your writing. Write a concluding statement at the end of your essay to wrap up your points.

Getting Started Tell children to begin writing their compare and contrast essay using their Venn diagram for guidance. Give them suggestions on how to develop their points with supporting evidence from each selection. Emphasize the importance of using complete sentences and correct grammar and conventions.

STEP 4 Evaluate Your Writing

Display the checklist below and have children use it to evaluate their compare and contrast essays. Circulate around the room and confer with individual children.

- ✓ Did I introduce my topic?
- ✓ Did I compare and contrast the families by telling how they are alike and different?
- ✓ Did I use facts from both selections to explain my points?
- ✓ Did I use clue words to explain the likenesses and differences?
- ✓ Does my concluding statement make sense?
- ✓ Did I use complete sentences?

Help children set goals and make a plan for improving in areas where their writing needs enhancement.

STEP 5 Revise and Publish

Help children follow through with their plans for revision. If time permits, have children trade compare and contrast essays and offer tips and suggestions for how to improve the writing.

Publishing Children can publish their essay by typing it on a computer and posting the printout on a wall display for their classmates to read.

Compare and Contrast Essay

Objectives

- Identify the characteristics of a compare and contrast essay.
- Write a compare and contrast essay, using facts and supporting details.
- Evaluate your writing.
- Revise and publish your writing.

Ⓒ Common Core State Standards

Writing 2. Write informative/ explanatory texts in which they introduce a topic, use facts and definitions to develop points, and provide a concluding statement or section.

STEP 1 Read Like a Writer

Review the key features of a compare and contrast essay listed below. Respond to any questions children might have.

Key Features of a Compare and Contrast Essay

- Compares two things by telling how they are alike
- Contrasts two things by telling how they are different
- Uses compare and contrast words to point out likenesses and differences
- Uses facts and definitions
- Provides a concluding statement

Choose a compare and contrast essay to model key features. Display the model for children to see and point out each of the key features you have discussed.

STEP 2 Organize Your Ideas

Writing Prompt In *A Froggy Fable* and "Ben the Bullfrog," you read about two frogs trying to find a happy home. Based on the stories, compare and contrast these two characters. Provide evidence from the texts to support your points. Use precise words to point out how the frogs are alike and different.

Think Aloud Your ideas will be more convincing if they are well organized. Think about each frog character: what they look like, what their hopes are, and how they interact with other animals. It can help to make a chart before you write. Label one side of the chart *Alike* and the other side *Different*.

Guided Writing Help children fill in their charts. Tell them that they will write one paragraph describing the likenesses and another paragraph describing the differences. Each paragraph will include facts and details that support the topic sentence.

STEP 3 Draft Your Writing

Have children use their charts to write a compare and contrast essay. Remind them of the key features of a compare and contrast essay.

Think Aloud It is important to include words that compare and contrast. Writers use them to signal how things are alike or different. Words that compare and contrast include *and, both, too, but, in contrast,* and *alike.*

Getting Started Tell children to begin writing their compare and contrast essay using their charts to keep them on track. Give them suggestions on where in the stories they can find supporting facts and details. Remind them to end with a concluding statement.

STEP 4 Evaluate Your Writing

Display the checklist below and have children use it to evaluate their compare and contrast essays. Circulate around the room and confer with individual children.

- ✓ Does the essay clearly compare and contrast two things?
- ✓ Are likenesses and differences clearly organized?
- ✓ Does the essay use compare and contrast words?
- ✓ Do I end with a conclusion?

Help children set goals and a plan for working on areas where their writing needs improvement.

STEP 5 Revise and Publish

Help children follow through with their plans for revision. If time permits, have children trade essays and offer suggestions for how to improve their writing.

Publishing After children have completed their final drafts, have them share their essays with the class.

Expository Essay

Objectives

- Develop an understanding of an expository essay.
- Write an expository essay.
- Use processes and strategies that good writers use.
- Evaluate your writing.
- Revise and publish your writing.

© Common Core State Standards

Writing 2. Write informative/ explanatory texts in which they introduce a topic, use facts and definitions to develop points, and provide a concluding statement or section.

STEP 1 Read Like a Writer

Review the key features of an expository essay listed below. Respond to any questions children might have.

Key Features of an Expository Essay

- Introduces a topic
- Explains and gives information about a topic
- Uses facts and details to develop points
- Presents information in an organized way
- Provides a concluding statement

Choose an expository essay to model key features. Display the model for children to see and point out each of the key features you have discussed.

STEP 2 Organize Your Ideas

Writing Prompt Briefly review *Horace and Morris but mostly Dolores* and "Good Kicking." These two selections involve boys and girls playing together. What kinds of things do children do together when they have fun? How does playing together help them get along? Write an expository essay that explains the kinds of things children play together, and how playing helps children get along.

Think Aloud Your information will be easier to understand if it is well organized. Look through *Horace and Morris but mostly Dolores* and "Good Kicking" and start a list of things that children play together. Then go back and add details from the texts to support your writing.

Guided Writing Help children begin their lists, and provide additional guidance with helping them find details and facts from both selections to support the items in their lists.

STEP 3 Draft Your Writing

Remind children of the key features of an expository essay. Have children use their lists to begin writing.

Think Aloud We can best organize an expository essay by using the questions from the writing prompt: *What kinds of things do children do together when they have fun? How does playing together help them get along?* We can use our lists to answer these questions as we write.

Getting Started Tell children to begin writing their expository essays using their lists to keep them organized. Give them suggestions on how to stay on the topic. Emphasize the importance of proper mechanics and conventions.

STEP 4 Evaluate Your Writing

Display the checklist below and have children use it to evaluate their expository essays. Circulate around the room and confer with individual children.

- ✓ Did I introduce my topic at the beginning?
- ✓ Did I use facts and details from the texts to develop my points?
- ✓ Did I present information in an organized way?
- ✓ Does my concluding statement make sense?

Help children set goals and a plan for improving in areas where their writing needs to be better.

STEP 5 Revise and Publish

Help children follow through with their plans for revision. If time permits, have children trade expository essays and offer suggestions for how to improve the writing.

Publishing Children can publish their expository essays by including drawings or photographs that depict children playing together.

Summary

Objectives

- Identify the characteristics of a summary.
- Write a summary, using facts and supporting details.
- Use processes and strategies that good writers use.
- Evaluate your writing.
- Revise and publish your writing.

Common Core State Standards

Writing 2. Write informative/explanatory texts in which they introduce a topic, use facts and definitions to develop points, and provide a concluding statement or section.

STEP 1 Read Like a Writer

Review the key features of a summary listed below. Respond to any questions children might have.

Key Features of a Summary

- Introduces a topic
- Gives information about a text in a shorter form
- Uses relevant facts and details
- Provides a concluding statement

Choose a summary that children have already read to model key features. Display the model for children to see and point out each of the key features you have discussed.

STEP 2 Organize Your Ideas

Writing Prompt *Red, White, and Blue: The Story of the American Flag* gives factual information about our country's flag. "You're a Grand Old Flag" is a song about the flag. Use what you learned from these selections to write a summary about the American flag. Provide evidence from the texts to support your points.

Think Aloud Keep your information organized. As you look through the texts, identify main events in the history of the American flag. Organize the events in a time line.

Guided Writing Help children create their time lines, including facts, details, and descriptive words and phrases from both texts.

STEP 3 Draft Your Writing

Have children use their time lines to write a summary. Remind them of the key features of a summary.

Think Aloud Use your time lines to help you determine three or four of the most important events in the history of the American flag. Use those events to include in your summary.

Getting Started Tell children to begin writing their summaries using their time lines as a guide. Remind them to use facts and details from the texts for support. Remind children to use proper spelling and grammar and to use complete sentences. Emphasize that children should end their summary with a strong concluding statement.

STEP 4 Evaluate Your Writing

Display the checklist below and have children use it to evaluate their summary. Circulate around the room and confer with individual children.

- ✓ Did I introduce my topic at the beginning?
- ✓ Did I use only important information on the topic?
- ✓ Did I tell about a real subject?
- ✓ Did I use relevant facts and details?
- ✓ Does my concluding statement make sense?

Help children set goals and a plan for improving in areas where their writing needs to be better.

STEP 5 Revise and Publish

Help children follow through with their plans for revision. If time permits, have children trade summaries and offer suggestions for how to improve the writing.

Publishing Children can share their work by posting their summaries on a poster, including a title, author name, and a drawing of the American flag.